£2·50

GW00683587

G. J. Churchward
A Locomotive Biography

G. J. Churchward
A Locomotive
Biography

BY

COLONEL H. C. B. ROGERS
O.B.E.

LONDON

GEORGE ALLEN & UNWIN LTD
Ruskin House   Museum Street

First published in 1975

© George Allen & Unwin Ltd 1975

ISBN 0 04 385061 8 hardback

Printed in Great Britain
in 11 point Plantin type
by Cox & Wyman Ltd,
London, Fakenham and Reading

TO MY WIFE
who travelled with joy
through Churchward's country
and found new friends in his relations

ACKNOWLEDGEMENTS

Without the help that I have received from many people it would not have been possible to write this book. If the great engineer, who is its subject, comes to life at all in these pages, it is due primarily to Mr W. N. Pellow, late Locomotive Running Superintendent of the Great Western Railway, Mr H. Holcroft, who described himself as Churchward's 'man for design', and Mr R. F. Hanks, who after serving under Churchward in a very junior capacity at Swindon eventually became Chairman of the Western Area Board of the British Transport Commission. My friend Harry Holcroft died at the age of ninety-one, shortly after sending me his comments on the draft Chapter 6 of this book. Mr W. N. Pellow, apart from the time and trouble he has devoted to correcting my work, has himself re-written sections where I have strayed from the truth or written mechanical rubbish. Mr R. F. Hanks has read nearly all my chapters and has provided me with much kindly comment and correction. Mr K. J. Cook, the last Great Western man to occupy Churchward's chair at Swindon, has given me invaluable aid with regard to some chapters which he was kind enough to read. Mr R. C. Bond, late Chief Mechanical Engineer of British Railways and subsequently Technical Adviser to the British Transport Commission, gave me particular help over the last two chapters. That great engineer Mr M. A. Chapelon has given me his opinion on G. J. Churchward and his engines, and has added much invaluable technical comment. And finally, my old friend Mr R. A. Riddles, late Vice-President of the LMS and then Member of the Railway Executive for Mechanical and Electrical Engineering, has given me his own appreciation of Churchward's locomotives and of those design features which he incorporated in his Standard Locomotives for British Railways.

Apart from these eminent locomotive engineers, there are many others who have given kindly assistance. Captain P. R. S. Churchward, probably G. J. Churchward's closest surviving relation, has told me a great deal about the history of this remarkable family. Mr E. Hannaford Hill, one-time 'tiger' of the Hill House coach, knows a great deal about G. J. Churchward's branch of the family; and Mr F. W. Robinson, who owns the Stoke Gabriel Garage, is the son of the Hill House coachman and played as a boy with G.J.C.'s unfortunate nephew. Mr B. G.

Churchward has sent me some useful notes about Churchwards overseas. Mr M. Beacom, owner of the Gabriel Court Hotel (the former Hill House) was most helpful in suggestions for local investigation. Mr G. W. Carpenter came as always to my help with books and papers, and Mr O. S. Nock kindly responded to my plea for help. I am pleased to be able to include a lady locomotive enthusiast in the person of Miss V. M. Brown, who produced for me sundry anecdotes about G. J. Churchward.

For illustrations I am indebted to British Railways and particularly to all those who helped me select photographs in the Chief Civil Engineer's Office at Paddington and in the Print Room at Swindon, and to Dr P. Ransome-Wallis, Mr C. R. H. Simpson, and Messrs Wilding & Son.

Finally, I must mention the enthusiastic encouragement of Mr Philip Unwin, my publisher, who has read and made his own kindly comments on every chapter in the book.

CONTENTS

ILLUSTRATIONS

PLATES

Illustrations

Chapter 1

Birth of a Genius

Stoke Gabriel is one of the prettiest of South Devon villages. It lies on the left bank of the lower reaches of the Dart, its houses clustering at the base and clinging to the sides of a hill that rises in curving contours from the river. Looking towards the village from the quay, the scene is dominated by the tower of the old parish church of St Mary and St Gabriel, around which huddle the tombs of many generations of Churchwards and of their Jackson and other relations. Older than all the graves in the churchyard—in fact the oldest thing in all the scenery except for river and hills—is a large and ancient yew tree, its great arms, now supported by props, stretching far out over many of the tombstones. Its age is unknown, but expert opinion places it as between 1,000 and 1,500 years; a tree which was old, perhaps hundreds of years old, at the time of the Norman Conquest. It could have been old when, in about the year 730 a Saxon on the western frontier of Wessex stood beneath it and looked across the Dart to Damnonia, the country of his Cornish enemies. It is not known when a church was first raised at this spot on an ancient frontier, but one was standing here in 1148. There is a tradition that a Stoke, or Stockade, was built by a Gabriel Churchward, or Cyrceweard (a name which the *Anglo-Saxon Chronicle* mentions in connection with the events of 948) to protect the local church and that he was the first man in the district to be baptised a Christian. The present church is of much more recent construction, but even so it antedates the Reformation by many years. Inside the church there is evidence of the long connection of the Churchward family with Stoke Gabriel; for in the south wall is a stained glass window, below which is a brass plate inscribed: 'To the Glory of God and in pious memory of the family of Churchward since 1484 of Hill in this parish. This was erected by Frederick Churchward of Hill, 29 September 1906.'

A great man this Frederick Churchward, last squire of Stoke Gabriel and owner of Hill House, high up on Stoke Hill. From 1882 till his retirement in 1906 he was Joint General Manager of the National Provincial Bank, with a second house at Blackheath, and in the summer he would drive down to Hill House in his own coach, staying with friends on the way. On the occasion of his presentation of the window, he was interviewed by Harold Ashton of the *Morning Leader*, who described him as follows: 'He is of medium height, portly, and gloriously ruddy. He is the squire in face, form, and vestment. A loose coat, flung back, discloses an ample waistcoat of a rich blue, with white chess-board squares on it, and the whole is tied together by a vast gold chain, with seals. The pockets have braided flaps. Knickerbockers of a correct and sporting cut, heather stockings, and spats over broad-soled boots complete the picture.'

The Churchwards had begun to build Hill House in 1484, but some ten minutes' walk away is Rowes Farm, probably the earliest Churchward property in Stoke Gabriel, and here lived Frederick's younger brother, George and his wife Adelina Mary who, a cousin, had been a Churchward before her marriage. Hill House was sold in the late 1920s and became the Gabriel Court Hotel, but Rowes Farm, though the house is somewhat changed in appearance, is still a pleasant Devonshire farm at the end of the narrow winding lane which serves as the main road from Totnes into Stoke Gabriel. It is perhaps typical of the many little manor houses which were built in Devon and which subsequently acquired the whitewashed exterior and utilitarian roof which conceal the distinguished ancestry of present-day farm-houses.

At Rowes Farm, George Jackson Churchward was born on 31 January 1857—at the beginning of a year in which there was to be anxiety all over England on account of the great mutiny of the Bengal Army. The birth was registered on 3 March 1857 in the sub-district of Paignton in the Registration district of Totnes. George Churchward, the baby's father, described himself as a yeoman, a common designation of the time to denote a countryman who owned and farmed his own broad acres. The baby's second name came from his paternal grandmother, for his grandfather John, father of Frederick and George, married Mary Ann Jackson—one of another Stoke Gabriel family, whose tombstones can be seen in the churchyard. John Churchward had died before the baby was born, but his widow, Mary Ann, was still living at Hill House.

George Jackson was not the only child of George and Adelina; there were two other sons, John and James, and two daughters named Mary and Adelina respectively after their mother. The little farm-house must have been fairly crowded at this time, for in the same year that

George Jackson was born, Adelina Mary's father, Matthew Churchward moved into it. He had owned White Hill Farm, about a mile away, but had retired and had been living in Myrtle Cottage in Stoke Gabriel.

George's children would have seen much of their cousins at Hill House; Frederick's son Charles and his daughters Gwendoline and May. There was also a second cousin, Paul Rycaut Stanbury Churchward who had been born in 1858 and whose father, William Henry, lived in Stoke Gabriel. William Henry's father, William, had been born at Hill House in 1784, and he and his brother John were sons of another John Churchward of Hill House.

It was perhaps inevitable that, amidst this beautiful district of hill and river, the younger George should have been brought up to enjoy the twin pursuits of fishing and shooting, and to acquire that love of the countryside which he shared with his great predecessor as locomotive chief of the Great Western, Sir Daniel Gooch. But in addition to these pleasures he soon showed an ability in mathematics and an interest in mechanical devices. When he was old enough he attended Totnes Grammar School, only a few miles from Stoke Gabriel. Here his mechanical interest would undoubtedly have been stirred by the sight of the locomotives designed by Daniel Gooch for the South Devon Railway which hauled the trains bound for Exeter or Plymouth into Totnes station.

To help the education of the Churchward boys, Frederick Churchward arranged instruction by a private tutor at Hill House during the school holidays. Charles in due course went to Harrow (where Winston Churchill became his fag); George junior was studying to make engineering his career; and Paul was cramming for Sandhurst. (Many years later, Brigadier-General Paul Churchward told his son Paul Rycaut Shordiche Churchward how brilliant George Jackson had been at mathematics.)

Cassiers Magazine published in 1904 a short biography of G. J. Churchward, which must have been cleared with him; and in this it was stated that a decided taste for engineering prompted him early in life to adopt it as his profession. He was therefore articled as a pupil to John Wright, under whose able tuition, combined with his inborn love of mechanics, was laid the foundations of his future career.[1]

John Wright was Locomotive, Carriage, and Wagon Superintendent of the South Devon Railway. It is apparent that G. J. Churchward had a high opinion of him as an engineer, and he must indeed have been able because Daniel Gooch had chosen him for the appointment.

The arrangement with John Wright was probably made by George

Jackson's father. It was an obvious choice because the South Devon Railway Locomotive Works were at Newton Abbot, only a few miles distant from Stoke Gabriel. In 1873, then, at the age of sixteen, G. J. Churchward started his career as a locomotive engineer. There had probably been a journey for an interview before the train carrying him to a brilliant future steamed out of Totnes Station on the short journey to Newton Abbot. Because of the local standing of his father and uncle, he probably travelled in a first-class compartment of a South Devon six-wheel broad-gauge carriage, and one suspects that a fishing rod reposed in the rack.

The South Devon Railway had been completed in 1849 from Exeter to Plymouth, with a short branch from Newton ('Abbot' was not added till March 1877) to Torquay. Isambard Kingdom Brunel, the brilliant engineer of the Great Western, was also Engineer of the South Devon, and the railway was built to his 'broad' or seven-foot gauge, so completing a route over which the same rolling stock could run from Paddington to Plymouth. From Exeter to Newton Abbot the line follows a lovely course by river estuaries and sea coast. From there on to Plymouth, however, it is inland and over gradients that are the steepest of any main line in Great Britain. These gradients are a legacy of the method of traction originally planned for the railway. On the advice of Brunel, the Directors decided to adopt the 'Atmospheric' system, which was already in apparently successful use on the Dalkey branch of the Dublin & Kingstown Railway, where it was claimed that running costs were only 7d per mile as compared with 1s 4d per mile with locomotive-hauled trains.

The Atmospheric system was invented by the engineers Samuel Clegg and the brothers Joseph and Jacob Samuda (though the latter died in 1844). Trains were propelled by a piston running in a pipe laid between the rails and attached to a special carriage by an arm for which a continuous slot was cut in the top of the pipe. The air was exhausted from the pipe in front of the piston by a series of steam pumps in stationary engine houses located at intervals of three to four miles along the track. The slot in the top of the pipe was closed in front of and behind the connecting arm by a valve in the form of a continuous leather flap; so that, with a vacuum in front of the piston, it was driven forward by the atmospheric pressure behind. The system eventually failed because no means could be found of preventing the deterioration of the leather flap and consequent leakage of air into the pipe.

At first many engineers, including Brunel, Cubitt, and Vignolles, were impressed with the invention and recommended its use. In 1845 the London & Croydon Railway was installing it on part of its system; and it was proposed for the East Coast route between Newcastle and Berwick, and for an extensive system in Kent. In 1846 the Windsor, Slough, & Staines Atmospheric Railway was projected; the Direct Portsmouth line was proposed as an Atmospheric route; and in Scotland there were proposals for an Edinburgh & Leith Atmospheric Railway, with trains at ten-minute intervals, and an Atmospheric line from Crianlarich to Loch Lomond; whilst two new Atmospheric companies arose in Ireland, the Belfast & Holywood and the Dublin & Sandymount.[2]

Basically the idea foreshadowed electric traction; for, like rope traction before it, power was developed in static power stations rather than by locomotives on the track. It was believed (correctly, if it had been successful) that, to such a form of traction, steep gradients would be less of an obstacle than they would be for locomotives. The system was therefore very attractive to the South Devon, for if steep gradients could be accepted between Newton Abbot and Plymouth, the cost of construction would be considerably reduced.

Atmospheric traction failed and was abandoned eight years before G. J. Churchward was born, but he would doubtless have heard all about it at Newton Abbot, and many relics of the system would still have been in evidence. It is perhaps of some interest that (with the doubtful exception of the Metropolitan-operated Hammersmith & City Line) electric traction was never installed on the Great Western Railway, and has not yet appeared on any of the lines of the Western Region of British Railways. One may well wonder whether this was due to the influence on Churchward of the Atmospheric failure. (Even the diesel locomotives ordered by the British Railways Western Region had hydraulic instead of electric drive.)

The South Devon Railway was opened between Newton and Totnes in 1847, before any section was ready for working by atmospheric power, and Brunel was intensely worried as to whether the steam locomotives supplied on hire by the Great Western for the operation of the line would be able to climb the fearsome gradients. Sir Daniel Gooch writes in his *Memoirs*:[3] 'I never saw Mr Brunel so anxious about anything as he was about this opening. Relying upon the atmospheric principle, he had made these steep inclines and he feared there might be difficulties in working them. These difficulties disappeared with the day of opening; all our trains went through very well, and at night it seemed a great relief to Mr Brunel to find it was so. He shook hands with me and thanked me in a very kind manner for my share in the day's work. He never forgot those who helped him in a difficulty.' From this it is apparent that Gooch was himself present to see his engines perform. These were almost certainly some of the little 2–4–0 goods locomotives of the *Leo* class, with 5 foot coupled wheels, which had been delivered in 1841–42.

On 5 May 1848 a further section of the South Devon was opened for passenger traffic between Totnes and a temporary station at Laira Green on the outskirts of Plymouth. The first train on the opening day was hauled by two of the *Leo* class 2–4–0s, *Pisces* and *Cancer*. The pilot engine, *Pisces*, was driven by Daniel Gooch and the train engine, *Cancer*, by M. C. Rea, who three years later succeeded Archibald Sturrock as Works Manager at Swindon.[4]

The *Leo* class engines were really too light for the South Devon, and indeed Daniel Gooch rebuilt them all before long as saddle tanks to overcome their lack of adhesion. To meet the needs of the line and its traffic, Gooch designed and built in 1849 two saddle tank engines with leading bogies named (in accordance with the Great Western practice of naming but not numbering locomotives) *Corsair* and *Brigand*. It is worth considering them for a moment because engines of this type were very likely the first that young George Churchward set eyes on, and they must have been among the first on which he worked when a pupil at Newton. They had 17 inch by 24 inch inside cylinders and coupled wheels 6 feet in diameter. The main frames were of the sandwich type and placed inside, but they did not extend forward of the coupled wheels on account of the bogie. The Gooch bogie was sited with its centre behind the smokebox, and its centre pin was fixed to a bracket on the underside of the boiler-barrel. The boiler formed the connection between the cylinders and the main frames, and the power from cylinders to driving axle was therefore transmitted through the boiler. (In practice this arrangement proved so unsatisfactory that engines so built were scrapped when their boilers wore out, and 4–4–0 tank engines supplied to the South Devon from 1866 had plate frames from front to back.)[5]

Corsair had a sledge brake between the driving wheels which acted on the rails; but it was not very successful because it tended to lift the engine at the back when it was applied and it sometimes fouled points and crossings. *Brigand*, therefore, had brake blocks on the trailing wheels instead. The driving, i.e. leading coupled, wheels were without flanges, and around the tops of both coupled and bogie wheels were the peculiar narrow splashers which were such a distinctive feature of Great Western broad-gauge engines.

There are particular aspects of these engines that which may have had some influence on Churchward's later thinking: their boilers were domeless, they had coupled wheels and bogies to give adhesion and flexibility over the gradients and curves of the Devonshire and Cornish lines, and their appearance was functional with little concession to beauty of line. The two locomotives were an immediate success, and it was apparent that Gooch had produced a brilliant solution to South Devon operating difficulties.

The Great Western's charges for hauling the SDR trains were 1s 4d a mile on the flat section between Newton and Exeter, and 1s 9d a mile on the hilly route between Newton and Plymouth. The South Devon became increasingly dissatisfied with this arrangement because, except for the two 4–4–0 tank engines, the locomotives were under-powered and train operation suffered. Gooch writes[6] that at the end of 1850 the South Devon wanted larger and more suitable engines, and that the Great Western, which was working the line with small ones, refused to build any new ones. Gooch therefore suggested to the South Devon that if they would offer him a ten-year contract to work the line he might be able to find partners to finance the building of suitable engines. The South Devon directors agreed, and with Brunel's help partners were found in Charles Geach of Birmingham and Edward Evans of the Haigh Foundry, Wigan.

Gooch-designed engines similar to *Corsair* and *Brigand* (which had, of course, been built for the Great Western) to work the South Devon traffic, but with coupled wheels 5 feet 9 inches in diameter instead of 6 feet. Twelve, called the *Comet* class, were built by four different firms, and Gooch, with his partners, started working the line in the autumn of 1851.

In 1854 Gooch had thirteen more of the 4–4–0 tank engines built by R. & W. Hawthorn for the Great Western, but with the smaller 5 foot 9 inch coupled wheels. They were named after the classical poets, and with *Corsair* and *Brigand* formed a group of fifteen engines designated the *Bogie* class. Three years later he provided four 0–6–0 saddle tank engines with 4 foot 9 inch wheels to work the South Devon goods traffic.

The contract came to an end in 1859, when Churchward was two years old, but it was renewed for a further period of seven years. In this new contract speed limits were imposed: these were, for passenger trains (excluding stops), 35 m.p.h. east of Newton and 20 m.p.h. west of it; and for goods trains, 20 m.p.h. on all parts of the railway

In this same year of 1859 the Cornwall Railway was opened from

Plymouth over the great bridge at Saltash to Truro. In addition, the South Devon's Torquay branch was extended by the opening of the first section of the Dartmouth & Torbay Railway to Paignton, and another South Devon subsidiary, the Devon & Tavistock Railway, was opened throughout.[7] Of the opening of the Cornwall Railway, Gooch said that as it was added to his contract he was of necessity a good deal in Devonshire and Cornwall.[8] More locomotives were required for the increased mileage and Gooch supplied twelve more 4-4-0 tank engines of the *Hawk* class, which differed from their predecessors mainly in having coupled wheels of 5 feet 6 inches and slightly smaller cylinders. In 1862-64 eight 0-6-0 goods saddle tanks were supplied, of which two had 4 foot 6 inch wheels and the others 4 feet 9 inches.

The Cornwall Railway was leased jointly to the Great Western, the Bristol & Exeter, and the South Devon Railways, but it maintained its separate existence until 1899. There were speed limits on it when it was opened of 30 m.p.h. for passenger trains and 15 m.p.h. for goods trains.

On all three of the new railways there were soon extensions to Falmouth, Kingswear, and Launceston, respectively, and for the additional route mileage Gooch delivered more of the *Hawk* class.

The Dartmouth & Torbay Railway was worked as part of the South Devon from the start. It was opened to Kingswear on 16 August 1864, and was connected to Dartmouth by a ferry across the River Dart. The seven-year-old George may well have seen something of the construction of this railway only a few miles away from his home. (It is of some interest that the section from Paignton to Kingswear is now under private ownership as the Torbay Steam Railway and is operated with ex-Great Western locomotives and carriages painted in GWR livery.)

Daniel Gooch's younger brother, William, had been appointed Locomotive Superintendent for the contractors and had established his Works at Newton. In 1857 Rea, Works Manager at Swindon, died and William Gooch was appointed to succeed him. Daniel Gooch says[9] that the Directors had promised him that when he retired William should have his job, provided that he took up this appointment as Works Manager at Swindon at the salary they offered. Daniel Gooch selected John Wright to succeed his brother, and in 1866, when the contract terminated, Wright became Locomotive, Carriage, and Wagon Superintendent of the South Devon Railway. His responsibilities, however, also included the Cornwall and West Cornwall Railways; for the South Devon bought all the forty contractors' locomotives, agreed with the Cornwall Joint Committee to work the Cornwall Railway, and under-

1   G. J. Churchward in about 1904. (*British Railways*)

2 *Above*: Rowes Farm, Stoke Gabriel, where G. J. Churchward was born. (*H. C. B. Rogers*)

3 *Right*: Hill House, Stoke Gabriel; now the Gabriel Court Hotel. (*H. C. B. Rogers*)

4 *Below*: Stoke Gabriel Church. The ancient yew is the round tree to the left of the tower. (*H. C. B. Rogers*)

took to work the West Cornwall Railway when its broad-gauge track had been completed.

The West Cornwall was the third of the principal railways whose trains were hauled by South Devon engines. It ran from Truro to Penzance, and in 1865 it had become the joint property of the Great Western, Bristol & Exeter, and South Devon. It had been constructed originally as a narrow, i.e. standard, gauge line; but its Act of incorporation required the installation of broad-gauge tracks as soon as this was requested by a connecting broad-gauge company. Alteration of the line to mixed gauge by laying a third rail was completed on 6 November 1866, and on that day the first broad-gauge goods train ran through to Penzance.

John Wright continued to order locomotives of Gooch's well-tried designs. Six 4–4–0 and two 0–6–0 saddle tank engines were ordered in 1866. The former were the *Pluto* class with 5 foot 8 inch coupled wheels, whilst the 0–6–0s, named *Romulus* and *Remus*, had 4 foot 9 inch wheels. These engines were needed for the West Cornwall trains; though they were not confined to that line because the South Devon's entire locomotive stock was used without discrimination over all three systems.

Increased freight traffic led John Wright to provide more 0–6–0 saddle tanks, and ten of these with 4 foot 9 inch wheels were built in 1872–73. They were known as the *Buffalo* class and, because the broad gauge was now clearly doomed, Wright so designed them that they could be easily converted to run on the standard gauge. (Delivery of these new engines would have been in progress when young Churchward arrived at Newton Abbot.) Two new 4–4–0 saddle tank engines, *Leopard* and *Stag*, were put into traffic in December 1872, with the same dimensions as the *Comet* class but of more modern design and also convertible. A further two, *Lance* and *Osiris* (replacing older engines with the same names), appeared in February 1875. None of these convertible engines was in fact converted when the broad gauge was abolished.

In addition to these standard types, there were eight little 4–4–0 tank engines with 3 foot wheels, used mainly for shunting on the Plymouth dock lines; three of them having inside cylinders and well tanks and the others outside cylinders and saddle tanks. There were also three inside cylinder side-tank engines of the Great Western *Sir Watkin* class, which had been built for working over the Metropolitan Railway in 1865–66.

When the South Devon contract ended, Sir Daniel Gooch was no longer Locomotive Superintendent of the Great Western Railway, for he had resigned in 1864. But he was not absent from this great company long, for at the end of the following year he was elected Chairman!

Gooch had retired because the amalgamation in 1863 of the South Wales and West Midland Railways with the Great Western brought new Directors to the Board whom he heartily disliked, and one of them, Richard Potter, became Chairman. Before vacating his appointment Gooch called upon Potter and reminded him of the promise that his brother William should succeed him. Potter said that he would do his best; however, he not only failed to support William Gooch, but also tried to set aside Joseph Armstrong (Daniel Gooch's Assistant on the Northern Division) in favour of Charles Sacré of the Manchester, Sheffield & Lincolnshire Railway. Gooch wrote to all the Directors with whom he thought he had influence, telling them that they should either appoint his brother or Armstrong. The Directors outvoted Potter and Armstrong was appointed. Gooch thought this the best solution, as his brother would not have worked well with the new Directors. However, he formed a small company to buy the Vulcan Foundry and had William appointed Managing Director, a position that he held until 1892.[10]

During 1865 and 1866 Daniel Gooch was engaged in laying the first successful Atlantic telegraph cable from Brunel's famous ship, the *Great Eastern*. For his triumphant success in this herculean task he was created a Baronet. Meanwhile, under Potter, the affairs of the Great Western Railway had not been going well, and towards the end of 1865 a reluctant Gooch was persuaded to succeed him as Chairman. Gooch had not known, however, how bad things were, and he was horrified to discover the state into which the financial side of the Company had drifted. He at once stopped all possible expenditure, cancelling amongst other things Potter's plan to build a large carriage works at Oxford. Describing Potter as a 'vain soft-headed fool, blown about by any wind', Gooch now instituted what was to be a long period of rigid economy.[11]

The financial crisis on the Great Western affected the South Devon and the other broad-gauge railway companies in the west; for the through train services were curtailed, and even the famous *Flying Dutchman* was taken off for eighteen months from the end of 1867.[12]

All South Devon engines were painted dark green and lined out in black. The 4-4-os had a sand box on top of the saddle tank in the position normally occupied by a steam dome, and behind the box was a wooden seat on which the fireman perched whilst he poured sand into a funnel inside the box whenever the rails were slippery. On the 0-6-os the sand box was in front of the engine above the smokebox door, presenting the fireman with a rather less dangerous task. The carriages of both South Devon and Cornwall Railways were painted in the same deep chocolate livery as those of the Great Western; but all the windows were square and the general appearance of the carriages was more rectangular.

E. L. Ahrons, who was in the Swindon Works from 1885 to 1890, knew the route from Newton Abbot to Penzance well in broad-gauge days. He says[13] that its succession of terrific banks made it the hardest route in the country. A great part of it was single line and, he adds, 'there was a considerable number of awesome wooden trestle viaducts, which caused an uncomfortable feeling when one travelled over them for the first time on the footplate'. Sir William Ackworth also knew it and he notes[14] that at Newton Abbot 'the character of the railway changes with an abruptness that is nothing short of startling'; and, 'As a sign of what is coming, the engine that had brought us from Bristol [one of Gooch's eight-foot 'singles'] leaves us. It is very doubtful if "she" could take her own weight any further, let alone attempting to draw the train. In her her stead an ugly unromantic creature, whose scientific name is "saddle tank", hooks on.' Perhaps no engines demonstrated the ability of Daniel Gooch as an engineer more than the ungainly tank locomotives that operated the traffic over these lines in Devon and Cornwall during the whole life of the broad gauge.

Such was the South Devon empire when John Wright's new pupil joined in 1873. Perhaps he was not sorry to leave Rowes Farm. As one can see today, it is a small place for two parents and five 'teenage' sons and daughters; especially when some of the latter have little in common. One might deduce that George senior was not very well off, as compared with his elder brother Frederick at Hill House. The pupillage to John Wright may have taken quite a large proportion of the money that George could spare for the education of his children; and certainly there was some resentment amongst Frederick's children that George Jackson should have been treated so much better than his brothers. James in due course emigrated to Australia. John, a dull personality compared to his brilliant brother George, married his first cousin Gwendoline and inherited Rowes Farm when his father died at the age of eighty-five. By that time the resentment had grown into a family estrangement, for Mary and Adelina were devoted to their brother George and detested Gwendoline. Frederick's other daughter, May, also married a Churchward cousin. This was George Dundas, the son of William Henry's brother Joseph. This George Churchward also became a railway engineer and, going out to China, built the

Tientsin-Tangshan Railway. Joseph, a remarkable character, had in 1854, three years before George Jackson's birth, acquired, in partnership with a Mr Jenkins, the mail contract between Dover and Calais and took over four of the Admiralty mail packets to operate it. In 1862 he lost the mail contract to the London Chatham & Dover Railway, but became Member of Parliament for Dover. Another son, Alaric Watts, entered into the service of the London Chatham & Dover Railway, became Marine Superintendent at Queenborough, and in 1889 was appointed Paris agent of the London Chatham & Dover. He continued in that post under the South Eastern & Chatham Railway until 1914 and died in 1929. There was yet another Churchward who rose to eminence in the railway world; this was William Patrick, the elder brother of Paul Rycaut Stanbury, who had a lot to do with Italian railways and was given an honour by the Italian Government for his work. It is rather remarkable that there should have been four Churchward cousins of the same generation who made their mark in a railway career.

At Newton Abbot young George Churchward soon showed his mechanical ingenuity, for in 1875, in conjunction with Richard Neville Grenville, another pupil of John Wright, he designed and built one of the earliest road motor cars. This was a three-wheeled vehicle with a single wheel in front, steered by a tiller. It was driven by a steam engine, also designed and built by the two of them, which used a small Merryweather fire-engine boiler to supply the steam. Many years later two members of the Newcomen Society, G. Allen and F. J. Bretherton, put this steam car into working order again. Some years ago R. F. Hanks saw it in the Works of John Allen & Sons (Oxford) Limited at Cowley, and from there it was eventually moved to the Science Museum.[15]

Churchward only spent three years at Newton Abbot, because the South Devon Railway, following the example of the Bristol & Exeter, agreed to amalgamate with the Great Western. On 1 February 1876 the Great Western Railway took over the working of the South Devon, the Cornwall, and the West Cornwall Railways, pending Parliament's confirmation of the amalgamation decision—a confirmation which was given in 1878. According to Gooch[16] this step was forced on the Great Western on account of the purchase by the London & South Western and the Midland Railways of the Somerset & Dorset Railway.

John Wright retired, probably some time in 1877 because Gooch writes on 6 April of that year: 'We went to Newton today and had lunch with John Wright.'[17] G. J. Churchward went to Swindon shortly after the Great Western took over to serve the last year of his pupillage under

Joseph Armstrong. As compared with Newton Abbot, prospects at Swindon for able and ambitious young men were of course considerably better; for not only was the Great Western the largest railway in the country, but Swindon's reputation already stood high in the locomotive world.

In popular opinion the Great Western was a broad-gauge line. In its earlier years this had been true, but it was no longer so in 1876. The West Country railways, which now became part of the Great Western system, were still entirely broad gauge, and it is conceivable that Churchward had not as yet travelled in a narrow, i.e. standard, gauge train. But the decision to abandon the broad gauge had been virtually taken ten years earlier.

At the General Meeting of 2 March 1866, the first at which he presided as Chairman, Sir Daniel Gooch said: 'There is no doubt that it has become necessary for us to look the matter of the narrow gauge fairly in the face. We have had within the past few days a memorial signed by nearly every firm of any standing in South Wales wishing that the narrow gauge might be carried out in their district. It is also pressing upon us in many other districts, and it will be necessary for us to consider how this matter should be dealt with. That it will be a costly question there can be no doubt. We cannot look at it without seeing that it involves a large expenditure of money. How best to meet and deal with that expenditure is a question the Directors will have to solve, and that probably before we meet again.'[18]

At the time of Gooch's statement the Great Western was already nearly half narrow gauge; for of the lines that it was working, 600 miles were broad gauge, 230 mixed, and 420 narrow. Gooch's statement sounded the death knell of the broad gauge, for after 1866 no new broad-gauge engines were built (though renewals or replacements of the famous 8 foot singles continued).

Conversions of various lines started in 1868. In March 1869 all trains on the route Oxford–Birmingham–Wolverhampton became narrow gauge, and the third rails on this previously mixed gauge track were taken up. In May 1870 it was decided to convert all the lines in South Wales to narrow gauge—a total track mileage of about 500—and this was carried out in May 1872. At the same time the mixed gauge, which already existed between Paddington and Didcot, was continued to Swindon and the line from Swindon to Gloucester was converted, so that there was now narrow-gauge communication throughout between Paddington and Milford Haven. At the end of the year the broad-gauge rails between Didcot and Oxford were removed. By 1876 all Great Western lines were either narrow or mixed gauge, and practically the only broad-gauge trains left were those between Paddington and the south-west. In that year, of course, the amalgamation brought a considerable increase in the Great Western's broad-gauge mileage, and the 8 foot singles, which had previously stopped at Bristol, ran through over the erstwhile Bristol & Exeter and South Devon systems to Newton Abbot.

The broad gauge was to continue between Paddington and Penzance for another sixteen years, but the vast majority of Great Western trains in 1876 ran on narrow-gauge tracks. Nevertheless, the broad-gauge expresses remained the aristocrats of the line and E. L. Ahrons writes: 'There was for many years a deep-rooted idea in Paddington minds that it was utterly impossible for a standard-gauge train to run as fast as a broad-gauge train.'[19]

At the time of the amalgamation the Great Western, thanks to Sir Daniel Gooch, had recovered from its crisis and was fairly prosperous. It gave an impression, perhaps, of conservative respectability, with a lofty suspicion of any change. Its character was reflected in its train services, for whilst the broad gauge *Flying Dutchman* was the fastest train in the world, many of the other services were appallingly slow.

It is unlikely that Churchward regretted the passing of the broad gauge. As a young engineer at the start of his career he would have been mainly interested in current and future design, and the development of broad-gauge equipment had come to a halt when he was nine years old. Sentiment in mechanical matters was not included in his make-up and he probably felt that the sooner the broad gauge was swept away the better it would be.

NOTES

1   *Cassier's Magazine*, **XXVII** (December 1904).
2   H. G. Lewin, *The Railway Mania and its Aftermath* (London, The Railway Gazette, 1936), pp. 15, 16, 24, 109–10, 141, 149–50, 228, 233, 240.
3   Sir Daniel Gooch, *Memoirs and Diary*, ed R. B. Wilson (Newton Abbot, David & Charles, 1972), p. 63.
4   E. T. MacDermot, *History of the Great Western Railway* (London, Great Western Railway Company, 1927), vol. II, pp. 217–18.
5   E. L. Ahrons, *The British Steam Railway Locomotive* (London, The Locomotive Publishing Co., 1927), pp. 69–70.
6   Gooch, op. cit., p. 67.
7   MacDermot, op. cit., vol. II, pp. 237*ff*

8   Gooch, op. cit., p. 75
9   Ibid., 93*ff*.
10 Ibid., p. 95.
11 Ibid., 108*ff*.
12 MacDermot, op. cit., vol. II, p. 40.
13 E. L. Ahrons, *Locomotive and Train Working in the Latter Part of the Nine-teenth Century*, ed L. L. Asher (Cambridge, W. Heffer & Sons, 1953), vol. IV, p. 19.
14 W. M. Ackworth, *The Railways of England* (London, John Murray, 3rd edn, 1889), pp. 260–1.
15 Sir William Stanier, 'George Jackson Churchward, Chief Mechanical Engineer, Great Western Railway', *Transactions of the Newcomen Society*, **XXX** (1960).
16 Gooch, op. cit., p. 220.
17 Ibid., p. 233.
18 MacDermot, op. cit., vol. II, p. 47.
19 E. L. Ahrons, *Locomotive and Train Working*, vol. IV, p. 30.

Chapter 2

Swindon and Sir Daniel Gooch

No biography of G. J. Churchward could be complete without some mention of the remarkable man who designed the engines amongst which Churchward started his railway career and who fashioned the environment amidst which Churchward was to spend the whole of his working and retired life.

At the age of nineteen Daniel Gooch joined the Works of Robert Stephenson & Company in Newcastle upon Tyne. He only spent a few months there, from January to October 1836, but during that time he made some drawings for two of the locomotives which were being made in Stephenson's Works for export. Gooch says that these engines were for a Russian railway of 6 foot gauge, and that he was delighted to have so much room to arrange the engine. He added that for some financial reason all the engines were not sent to Russia, and the two for which he had made the drawings were converted to the 7 foot gauge for the Great Western Railway as the *Morning Star* and the *North Star*. Gooch was much impressed when making these drawings with the importance of a wider gauge, and thus became an early advocate of the broad-gauge system.[1]

Later opinion has it that Gooch's memory was at fault and the two engines which went to the Great Western were intended for the 5 foot 6 inch gauge New Orleans Railway. Certainly two engines built by Robert Stephenson & Company for that railway were left on the firm's hands owing to a financial panic. However, there is a third story, for Robert Stephenson in his evidence before the Gauge Commission said: 'I know that the gauge of American railways is the same as our own 4 feet $8\frac{1}{2}$ inches. At one time they commenced laying down a line with a gauge of 6 feet for which the engines eventually used on the Great Western were intended; and after they had laid some considerable distance they abandoned it and went back to the old gauge of 4 feet $8\frac{1}{2}$ inches.'[2] Gooch stuck to his story, and in 1880 he wrote on a drawing which he had of the Russian engines: 'These engines were built by Messrs R. Stephenson & Company, Newcastle, for a Russian order, 6 feet gauge, but were not delivered. The Great Western bought them for £3000 each. The "North Star" in 1837, the "Morning Star" later, the gauge being altered to 7 feet.'[3] One may well feel that in a matter of such importance in his professional life, Gooch's memory did not fail him. The origin of the *North Star* is of considerable interest because she was, to a large extent, the model from which all subsequent broad-gauge engines on the Great Western were developed.

Towards the end of July 1837 Gooch, then working under his brother Tom on the Manchester & Leeds Railway, heard that Brunel wanted someone to take the post of Locomotive Engineer on the Great Western Railway, and immediately wrote and sent off an application. On 2 August he had a reply from Brunel saying that he was coming north and would see him. On 9 August Brunel called at the Manchester & Leeds offices, saw Gooch, engaged him on the spot, and asked him to go to the Great Western at once. Daniel Gooch was then just short of his twenty-first birthday.

Gooch soon found that he was faced with no easy task. Brunel, who had no experience as a locomotive engineer, had original ideas on what locomotives should be like. Gooch wrote: 'I was not much pleased with the design of the engines ordered, they had very small boilers and cylinders and very large wheels. . . . I felt very uneasy about the working of these machines, feeling sure they would have enough to do to drive themselves along the road. The idea Mr Brunel acted upon was to get a slow speed in the piston with a high velocity in the wheel, and this was right enough if the power of the cylinders and boiler had been at all in proportion.'[4] In fact, the only reliable engine at his disposal was the *North Star.*

Gooch's fears about the engines were only too well founded, and he writes: 'The failure of so many engines made the Directors very anxious and they called upon me, apart from Mr Brunel, to make them a report on each engine.'[5] It was an embarrassing position because his own chief, Brunel, had been responsible for ordering them. However, he considered that he had no choice and submitted a report in which he condemned the design and construction of the majority of the engines. The report alarmed the Directors, and Brunel wrote an angry letter to Gooch. Nevertheless he realised that Gooch was right and gave his full support when, shortly afterwards, the Directors instructed Gooch to prepare designs for new locomotives.

33

From experience with, and experiments on the *North Star*, Daniel Gooch had already decided the type of locomotive required. Although a sound and reliable engine, he had not been satisfied with *North Star's* performance, but he had improved it considerably by altering the blast pipe. He increased the size of this and took care that the steam was discharged up the centre of the chimney. He says: 'It was wonderful how much the larger size freed the cylinders and the care in discharging it still enabled us to get plenty of steam.' Brunel thought that the orifice of the blast pipe should be made in the shape of a cross, and most of Christmas Day he and Gooch worked by themselves in the coppersmith's shop making one of this shape; 'but', says Gooch, 'nothing succeeded so well as the plain round orifice'.[6] By freeing the cylinders Gooch no doubt meant the lessening of the back pressure, and it showed his appreciation of the importance of exhaust design. At the same time the basic soundness of Brunel's idea was to be shown many years later when André Chapelon designed his Kylchap exhaust.[7]

Gooch says that he took great pains with the drawings of his engines, 'giving every detail much thought and consideration'. His offices were not in Swindon but at Paddington, and here was also his Chief Draughtsman, Thomas Russell Crampton, whom Gooch describes as a 'clever fellow'. Crampton's own indirect influence on Churchward's four-cylinder locomotives is discussed later in this book. The result of Gooch's work was, he says, 'designs for two classes of engines, one with a 7 foot driving wheel, 15 inch cylinders, and 18 inch stroke, and another with 6 foot wheels, 14 inch cylinders, and 18 inch stroke, both with ample boiler power; and I may with confidence, after these engines have been working for twenty-eight years, say that no better engines for their weight have been constructed either by myself or others. They have done, and continue to do, admirable duty.'[8] It was a proud but well justified boast. Gooch probably gives the reason for their success in his mention of 'ample boiler power'. It was a lesson from Gooch's designs that Churchward may well have learned during his pupillage, because the efficiency of their boilers was perhaps the outstanding feature of his own engines.

When Gooch's drawings were completed he had them lithographed and their specifications printed. In addition he produced iron templates for those parts which it was essential should be interchangeable. All these were supplied to various engine builders. This, it is believed, is the first instance of such standardisation of parts;[9] and standardisation was to be another policy which Churchward pursued on the Great Western.

Gooch's new engines were based largely on the *North Star*, being of the 2–2–2 type with slotted outside sandwich frames, made up of 3 inch thick planking covered on each side with half-inch iron plates. But, unlike the *North Star*, the boilers were domeless, for Gooch did not like steam domes. To get his steam space he fitted the high dome-shaped firebox casing often termed 'Gothic'. There were sixty-two 7 foot engines and twenty-one 6 foot, the former being designated the *Firefly* class and the latter the *Sun*. Gooch followed these with eighteen *Leo* class 2–4–0 goods engines and four 0–6–0s for heavy goods work; both having 5 foot coupled wheels.[10]

Daniel Gooch was very relieved when his own engines began to arrive in March 1940. He says that they gave general satisfaction and that the speed at which the trains could be worked could now be calculated with some certainty and with reasonable assurance that the locomotives would not break down. In fact the *Fireflies* had 'no difficulty in running at 60 m.p.h. with good loads.'[11]

In 1840, with the Great Western main line nearing completion and agreements having been made to lease the Bristol & Exeter and the Cheltenham & Great Western Union Railways, 'it became necessary', writes Gooch, 'to furnish larger works for the repair, etc., of our stock. I was called upon to report on the best situation to build these works, and on full consideration I reported in favour of Swindon, it being the junction with the Cheltenham branch and also a convenient division of the Great Western line for engine working. Mr Brunel and I went down to look at the ground, then only green fields, and he agreed with me as to its being the best place.'[12]

Brunel asked Gooch to submit his recommendation in writing, which he did on 13 September 1840. The following are the main points in his report:

'According to your wish I give you my views of the best site for our principal engine establishment, and in doing so I have studied the convenience of the Great Western Railway only, but also think the same point is the only place adapted for the Cheltenham and Great Western. The point I refer to is the Junction at Swindon of the two lines.

'The only objection I can see to Swindon is the bad supply of water. There is also an apparent inequality of distance or duty for the engines to work—but which is very much equalised when the circumstances attending it are taken into account. I find the actual distances are as $76\frac{1}{2}$ to 41 and the gradients are for the short distance of 41 miles a rise of

318 feet . . . and for the 76½ miles a rise of 292 feet. . . . Swindon being the point at which these gradients change, the different gradients necessarily require a different class of engine, requiring for the Bristol end a more powerful one than for the London end.

'That power can only be obtained conveniently by reducing the diameter of the Driving Wheels, therefore, supposing we work between Swindon and Bristol with 6 foot wheels, and between Swindon and London with 7 foot wheels, there will actually be very little difference between the work required of the two engines. . . . It would also divide the pilot engines very nearly equally, as Reading being the first station where a pilot engine would be kept, say 36 miles, the next distance, to Swindon, would then be 41 miles, and on to Bristol another 41. . . .

'It has also the great advantage of being on the side of a canal communicating with the whole of England, and by which we could get coal and coke, I should think at a moderate price.'[13]

Gooch's recommendation, supported by Brunel, was approved by the Directors as follows: 'That the Principal Locomotive Station and Repairing Shops be established at or near the Junction with the Cheltenham and Great Western Union Railway at Swindon.'

Before the coming of the Great Western Railway, Swindon had been nothing more than a pleasant little country town with a corn exchange, a small cattle market, and a total population (in 1831) of 1,742. Few travellers passed through it, for the great coach routes from London ran south of it to Bath and Bristol and north of it to Cheltenham and Gloucester. Commerce had however reached it some twenty years before by the opening of the canal to which Gooch refers.

Following the Industrial Revolution, there was an extensive development of inland water transport so that the coal required to operate the new factories could be distributed. Rivers were improved for navigation and an extensive network of canals was built. In that part of England which was to become Great Western country there was a need to connect the Rivers Severn and Thames, so providing communication between the latter and the canal system in the Midlands. This connection was made in 1789, when the Thames & Severn Canal Company bored the Sapperton tunnel, two miles long, through a spur of the Cotswolds to take their canal from the Stroud Valley to the Thames at Inglesham near Lechlade. In 1810 the Kennet & Avon Canal was opened, connecting Bristol and Bath, through Newbury, with Reading and the Thames. At the same time the Wiltshire & Berkshire Canal was built from the Kennet & Avon, near Bath, to the Thames at Abingdon, passing close to Swindon. These two canals distributed coal from the Somerset coalfield. In 1819 Swindon suddenly became an important canal centre when the 9-mile North Wiltshire Canal was completed, joining the Wiltshire & Berkshire with the Thames & Severn near Cricklade. This enabled the difficult section of the Thames above Oxford to be cut out, and the main route from the Severn to the Thames was now through the Sapperton tunnel, via Cricklade, Swindon, Abingdon, and so on to London.[14]

The railway locomotives of the time burnt coke, and it was the practice of each railway to produce its own by processing the raw coal in coke ovens. Gooch intended to get his coal from the Rhondda Valley, whence it would be carried by sea from Cardiff to Bristol. Coke ovens at Bristol would supply fuel to the whole line (including the Bristol & Exeter Railway, which the Great Western was to operate). The existing small establishment at West Drayton for producing coke would then close down.

Brunel and Gooch were impressed with the capacity of the North Wiltshire Canal to bring supplies from any point in England, so that they could envisage not only the repair of rolling stock, but a works which could undertake new construction. Accommodation would be needed for enginemen, artisans, and labourers, as well as for the staff of Swindon station; and this would entail an estate to include houses, the Company's offices, and various facilities. This was agreed to by the Board, and the estate which grew up was the nucleus of the eventual New Swindon.

The site selected for the Works was in the angle formed by the Great Western main line and the branch to Cheltenham, just west of the bridge carrying the former over the North Wiltshire Canal. The plan of the shops was unusual, for it was in the style of a corral, or enclosure for the protection of cattle from rustlers. The various shops were connected end on, so that their outer walls formed the perimeter of a rectangle, and the space enclosed by their inner walls was used for the safe storage of loose plant and materials. There was a lot of shop space, particularly for smiths. There was a steam hammer, and there were shops for boiler-makers, carpenters, and coppersmiths. There were wagon shops, a turning shop, an erecting shop for new engines, a repair shop (which joined on to the running shed), offices, and stores. There was no iron foundry, for at that time it was still the practice to draw molten metal direct from blast furnaces to produce iron castings. The day of the cupola and the supply of pig iron for re-melting and pouring into moulds on site had yet to come.[15]

Gooch's comment on the opening of the Works is brief: 'We started the machinery at the Swindon Works on the 28 November 1842. A. Sturrock was our local manager; but the Works were not put into regular operation until Monday 2 January 1843.'[16] Archibald Sturrock was a young man aged twenty-six whom Gooch had met and made friends with in 1835, when they were both at the Dundee Foundry, Gooch as a draughtsman and Sturrock as an apprentice. Gooch invited Sturrock to come and assist him at Bishop's Road, Paddington, to keep the miscellaneous lot of locomotives ordered by Brunel in some sort of running order, and when Swindon Works were ready Sturrock was sent there to take charge. Later he was appointed Locomotive Superintendent of the Great Northern Railway, the Works of which at that time were at Boston. In 1845 HRH the Duke of Cambridge, uncle of Queen Victoria, travelled to Swindon to see the Works, accompanied by Lord Barrington who was Deputy Chairman of the Great Western. Gooch found 'the old Duke full of questions and endless talk. He seemed very pleased with what he saw'.[17]

The first locomotive to be built at Swindon was *Premier*, completed in February 1846 and one of a class of twelve six-coupled goods engines built during 1846–47, the last to run with the haycock, or 'Gothic', firebox casing. The boilers, however, were made by an outside firm[18] and the first engine to be built completely at Swindon was, appropriately, the prototype of the eight-foot 'Singles'—the famous express locomotives which come to mind whenever one thinks of the broad gauge.

In 1845 the Gauge Commission began the task with which it had been charged of assessing the rival merits of the broad and narrow, i.e. standard, gauges. Much evidence was taken by the Commissioners from supporters of both systems and from persons who favoured neither. Finally a series of practical tests was held in which trains were hauled by both broad and narrow gauge engines. Gooch's engines showed their marked superiority over their rivals; but he thought he could do still better and, in anticipation of a renewal of the contest in 1846, he proposed an engine with 8-foot driving wheels and 18 inch by 24 inch cylinders. The Great Western Board gave him instructions to build it, and, Gooch says, 'as it was important to get it to work before the next session of Parliament, when a renewal of the fight would take place, I arranged for night and day work upon her, and had her finished thirteen weeks from the day of getting the orders; probably as quick a job as was ever done. She was first tried at the end of April 1846, and on 13 June we made a sensational trip with her to Bristol with a load of 100 tons. Mr Russell and the Directors and Brunel went down. A dinner was given to a large party at Bristol and a good deal of speech-making took place. 'We attained a steady speed of 62 m.p.h. with this load; the distance to Swindon was done in 1 hour 18 minutes, and to Bristol in 2 hours 12 minutes, including stoppages. Mr Russell called this a "great fact", and it was a great fact. Had we had this engine ready in time for the gauge experiments, how different would the results have been; although I don't suppose it would have altered the report. We called the engine the *Great Western*. She was built on six wheels, but, finding the weight too much on the leading wheels, I put another pair forward.'[19] This addition made the engine a 4–2–2.

Although the prototype of the succeeding *Iron Duke* class, *Great Western* differed from them in various particulars. The most important distinguishing feature was the haycock firebox. This was an expensive thing to make and the *Iron Dukes* had a raised firebox casing to provide steam space. On the top of the firebox casing were the safety valves, enclosed in a cylindrical cover of polished brass with a rim at the top and a square base which was nicknamed at Swindon the 'squashed bonnet box'. The wood lagging of the boiler was later covered with sheet iron plates encircled by polished brass bands. (The raised firebox casing, domeless boiler, and brass safety valve cover were all adopted later by Churchward.)

One of the *Iron Dukes*, the *Lord of the Isles*, was shown in the Great Exhibition of 1851. Gooch writes: 'The Great Western Company sent a locomotive, the *Lord of the Isles*, one of our large class of passenger engines, and I am safe in saying she was a beautiful job and has since done her work on the line satisfactorily. This cannot be said for most of the engines exhibited. I got a medal for her, but the highest class medal was given to Crampton for an engine certainly the most faulty in construction exhibited.'[20] However, Gooch was doing his former Chief Draughtsman an injustice. What he did not appreciate (and nor did anybody else) was the excellent steam circuit of Crampton's design, which was responsible for the long and successful career of so many of his engines on the Continent. A long time afterwards, and just over a year before his death, Gooch wrote in his diary on 16 July 1888:

'Dean gave me a very fine photograph of the old locomotive the *North Star*. She was one of those that opened the line, and we have kept her in a building built for the purpose at Swindon as a specimen of the engine of the period. I feel a great interest in this old engine and am glad to have so good a photograph of her. There is also a good photograph of the *Lord of the Isles*, an eight-wheel engine which was in the 1851 Exhibition. This was one of a new and powerful class of engine I built about that period. Several of them are still doing our express broad-gauge work and are equal in every respect to any we have since built. The *Lord of Isles* is also put away at Swindon to be preserved as a specimen of this class of engine.'[21]

Iron Duke, the first of the engines with round-top fireboxes, was so named because it ran its trial trip on the Duke of Wellington's birthday. Subsequent batches of these engines differed in details, such as wheel base and boiler dimensions. A few were rebuilt and a number were replaced by new engines carrying the same name. The 8 foot 'Singles' were the first engines to be fitted with the Gooch valve gear for expansive working, in place of the old gab motion, which did not allow any alteration in the point of cut-off.

Churchward would have known all of these most famous of broad-gauge engines, for they were hauling the West of England expresses through Swindon during his first sixteen years there. They are listed in full, therefore, at the end of this chapter. Originally they ran between Paddington and Swindon only; then, in 1852, they were also working the Paddington–Birmingham expresses, extended two years later to Wolverhampton. In 1869, when the line north to Birmingham was narrowed, they were again restricted to the Paddington–Swindon section —the trains west of Swindon being hauled by the 4–4–0 *Waverley* class. But after the amalgamation of 1876 they took over all the major expresses between Paddington and Newton Abbot and monopolised them until the disappearance of the broad gauge in 1892.[22]

E. L. Ahrons was a pupil under Dean at Swindon from 1885 to 1888, and from then till 1892 he was an inspector of materials attached to the Swindon drawing office. During Ahron's time these broad-gauge express engines were repaired under the chargemanship of a Mr William Cave, an exceedingly popular character with an encyclopaedic knowledge of the *Iron Duke* class. There were no drawings of these engines because all the dimensions had been altered since the original drawings had been made in 1847. Ahrons says that in about 1888 new drawings for the engines were begun, because it was considered advisable to have some record, but William Cave had to be consulted about every dimension that found its way into the drawings. He adds, 'This work formed one of the drawing office "stock jobs", and I am not sure that they were ever completed. A good many of us did bits at them until called away to something more urgent.'[23] It is nice to think that G. J. Churchward must have been well acquainted with William Cave.

THE EIGHT-FOOT 'SINGLES'

NAME	BUILT	REBUILT	CEASED WORK	NEW ENGINE	REBUILT	CEASED WORK
Great Western	1846		1870	1888		1892
Iron Duke	1847		1871	1873		1892
Great Britain	1847	1870	1880	1880		1892
Lightning	1847		1878	1878		1892
Emperor	1847		1873	1880		1892
Pasha	1847		1876			
Sultan	1847		1874	1876		1892
Courier	1848		1877	1878	1888	1892
Tartar	1848		1876	1876		1892
Dragon	1848		1872	1880		1892
Warlock	1848		1874	1876	1888	1892
Wizard	1848		1875			
Rougemont	1848		1879			
Hirondelle	1848		1873	1873		1890
Tornado	1849		1881	1888		1892
Swallow	1849		1871	1871		1892
Timour	1849		1871	1873		1892
Prometheus	1850		1888	1888		1892
Perseus	1850		1880			
Estafette	1850		1884			
Rover	1850		1871	1871	1888	1892
Amazon	1851		1877	1878		1892
Lord of the Isles	1851		1884			
Alma	1854		1872	1880		1892
Balaclava	1854		1871	1871		1892
Inkermann	1855		1877	1878		1892
Kertch	1855		1872			
Crimea	1855		1876	1878		1892
Eupatoria	1855		1876	1878		1892
Sebastopol	1855		1880	1880		1892
Bulkeley	1880					1892

NOTES

1 Sir Daniel Gooch, *Memoirs and Diary*, ed R. B. Wilson (Newton Abbot, David & Charles, 1972), p. 24.
2 Samuel Sidney, *Gauge Evidence* (London, Edmonds, 1846), p. 119.
3 J. G. H. Warren, *A Century of Locomotive Building* (Newcastle upon Tyne, Andrew Reid, 1923), p. 340.

4 Gooch, op. cit., p. 28.

5 Ibid., p. 35.

6 Ibid., p. 38.

7 Colonel H. C. B. Rogers, *Chapelon: Genius of French Steam* (London, Ian Allan, 1972), pp. 22–3.

8 Gooch, op. cit., p. 35.

9 Ibid., p. 35; and H. Holcroft, *An Outline of Great Western Locomotive Practice* (London, Locomotive Publishing Company, 1957), p. 2.

10 Ibid., pp. 2–5.
E. T. MacDermot, *History of the Great Western Railway*, vol. I, *The Locomotive and Carriage Departments* by E. L. Ahrons (London, Great Western Railway, 1927), p. 754.

11 Gooch, op. cit., p. 40.

12 Ibid., p. 40.

13 E. T. MacDermot, op. cit., pp. 120–1.

14 H. Holcroft, letter to the author.

15 Ibid.

16 Gooch, op. cit., p. 44.

17 Ibid., p. 48.

18 MacDermot, op. cit., pp. 770–1.

19 Gooch, op. cit., pp. 53–4

20 Ibid., p. 67.

21 Ibid., p. 351.

22 MacDermot, *History of the Great Western Railway*, vol. II, p. 513.

23 E. L. Ahrons, *Locomotive Working in the Latter Part of the Nineteenth Century*, vol. IV, ed L. L. Asher (Cambridge, W. Heffer & Sons, 1953), p. 13.

Chapter 3

The Armstrong Régime

On 12 October 1921 George Jackson Churchward became the first Honorary Freeman of the Borough of Swindon, and this recognition of his great services to the community was the culmination of a tradition that was started by the first of all locomotive superintendents of a railway. New Shildon, like New Swindon, grew up on a bare piece of countryside, not far from the ancient township of the same name. In May 1826 Timothy Hackworth, 'Superintendent of the Permanent and Locomotive Engines' of the Stockton & Darlington Railway, arrived there to take up his residence. New Shildon, like New Swindon, was at a point where a change was made in the haulage of the trains; it was at the foot of Brusselton Hill, up and down which trains were worked by ropes powered by the stationary engine at the top. Locomotive working was confined to the Shildon–Stockton section of the railway. At the time when the Hackworth family moved into a temporary house (pending the building of a better one by the Company) the only other structures were three more houses, the railway repair shops, and a small engine depot without a roof. Only about twenty men were initially employed, but the rapid construction of workmen's cottages soon enabled an increase of the staff to fifty, of whom a few were skilled mechanics. From the first, Timothy Hackworth took an intense interest in his work people and their families. He was a very religious man, a Wesleyan preacher, and he opened his house for weekly services. Through his efforts a Methodist chapel was built at Shildon in 1829 and another in New Shildon in 1831. Mrs Hackworth assisted her husband in all his schemes for the welfare of the workmen and their wives and children.[1] The centenary of Hackworth's death was observed in Shildon in July 1950, and a statue to his memory now stands in Shildon Recreation Ground in recognition of both his mechanical genius and his great work as a philanthropist.

Thomas Armstrong, who had settled at Newburn-on-Tyne in 1824, became friends with George Stephenson and Timothy Hackworth,

43

both of whom were born at near-by Wylam-on-Tyne. Two of Thomas's six sons died young; the remaining four all became engineers and two of them were destined to achieve high position on the Great Western Railway. These two were Joseph (born 1816) and George (born 1822). Joseph went to school in Newcastle, and during this time he had opportunities to see locomotives at work on the Wylam, Killingworth, and other colliery railways. He became enthusiastic about steam locomotives and decided to take up railway engineering as a career. Stephenson and Hackworth encouraged Joseph in his ambitions and there are reasons for believing that Hackworth gave him opportunities to learn engine driving on the Stockton & Darlington Railway. Certainly Joseph came under the influence of Timothy Hackworth and became infected with his ideas on the care and management of men.[2]

Thirteen miles north of Newcastle, at Bedlington, Daniel Gooch was born in the same year as Joseph Armstrong. His father, John Gooch, was also a friend of George Stephenson, and John Gooch's mother was the daughter of Michael Longridge of Newburn.[3] It is conceivable that John Gooch and Thomas Armstrong were acquainted, though there is no mention of it in Daniel Gooch's memoirs. Joseph probably passed on his enthusiasm to his younger brother George, for in later life George Armstrong told H. Holcroft that he used to run for miles alongside the engine *Puffing Billy* on the Wylam Colliery Railway.[4]

In 1836, aged twenty, Joseph Armstrong was an engine driver on the Liverpool & Manchester Railway. After four years on that line he was apparently attracted by the greatly improved locomotives designed by John Gray, Locomotive Superintendent of the Hull & Selby Railway, for he left the Liverpool & Manchester and got a similar job on the Hull & Selby. George, by this time, was employed at the Walbottle Colliery and, doubtless at his brother's suggestion, he left there and joined Joseph on the Hull & Selby. Gray in due course promoted Joseph to be foreman at the Hull running sheds. In 1845 John Gray was appointed Locomotive Superintendent of the London & Brighton Railway (which in the following year amalgamated with the London & Croydon to become the London Brighton & South Coast Railway) and took the Armstrong brothers with him; Joseph becoming a foreman at Brighton. In 1847, however, John Gray left the LBSCR. He was succeeded by S. Kirtley, who a few months later was succeeded in turn by J. C. Craven, The new Locomotive Superintendent seems to have been domineering, ruthless, and unpopular. It does not appear that the Armstrongs liked him for they left almost immediately; George to be an engine driver on one of the French railways which in 1851 amalgamated to form the Nord, and Joseph to be Assistant Locomotive Superintendent, under Edward Jeffreys, of the Shrewsbury & Chester Railway at Saltney near Chester. George was only a short time in France before the Revolution of 1848 caused him to leave the country and to rejoin his brother as an engine driver on the Shrewsbury & Chester. Not long afterwards Jeffreys left the S&CR and Joseph succeeded him as Locomotive Superintendent.[5]

In 1849 the Shrewsbury & Birmingham Railway was opened, and it and the Shrewsbury & Chester were operated as one system. The locomotives of the S&BR were provided and repaired under contract, but the contract expired in 1853, and Joseph Armstrong was moved to Wolverhampton and placed in charge of the locomotives of both railways. In the following year the two railways were amalgamated with the Great Western, and the Stafford Road Works, which had been established at Wolverhampton for their joint needs, became the headquarters of the Great Western (standard gauge) Northern Division, with Joseph Armstrong in charge. George, in the meantime, had been promoted foreman.[6]

The Wolverhampton Stafford Road Works had been planned only for the stabling and maintenance of rolling stock, because the two little companies were content to purchase their locomotives, carriages, and spare parts from private firms. This did not, of course, suit the Great Western, and the Company intended that Stafford Road should manufacture rolling stock for the standard gauge. This entailed extensive re-arrangement which took several years.[7]

About a year after the amalgamation William Dean started his railway life as an apprentice at Wolverhampton, and was soon to impress Joseph Armstrong, as Joseph himself had impressed Gray.

By 1858 Stafford Road Works had been sufficiently modified for new construction to start, and Joseph Armstrong built two 2-2-2 passenger engines to his own design; following these with similar but rather larger engines in 1860. All four showed the influence of Gray. In 1863 he built another 2-2-2, No. 110, which departed from Gray's practice by having double plate frames throughout. It was in fact the forerunner of the *Sir Daniel* and later designs.[8]

The amalgamation of the West Midland Railway with the Great Western in 1863 brought more standard-gauge route and stock; with the result that further extensions were necessary at Stafford Road Works to enable them to meet the new demands. The withdrawal of the broad gauge north of Oxford made additional space available, and the consequent enlargement of the Works greatly increased the capacity for new construction. In 1863–64 Joseph Armstrong produced six 2–4–0 passenger engines, as well as a number of saddle tank engines for both passenger and goods working. This marked the end of Joseph's time at Wolverhampton, for with Daniel Gooch's retirement he succeeded him at Swindon. J. Gibson, the Carriage & Wagon Superintendent, also retired, and at the request of the Directors Armstrong took over his job as well, becoming the first Locomotive, Carriage & Wagon Superintendent of the Great Western Railway. George Armstrong succeeded his brother as Northern Divisional Locomotive Superintendent, with William Dean as his Assistant and Manager of Stafford Road Works.[9]

On taking up his new appointment Joseph Armstrong decided that he would not emulate Daniel Gooch in working and residing at Paddington, but would, like Timothy Hackworth, live near the Swindon Works and establish his office there. The Company agreed and built him a new house which Joseph named *Newburn* after the home of his childhood. Gooch, with his own Newburn-on-Tyne ancestry, doubtless approved of the choice. As the home of the head of Great Western locomotive affairs during the régimes of Armstrong, Dean, and Churchward, the house was destined to achieve greater fame than the village. And when that Great Western enthusiast Sir William Stanier became Chief Mechanical Engineer of the London Midland & Scottish Railway he not only used the name for his home in Chorley Wood but transferred it to his new home when he moved to Rickmansworth.

As soon as he had settled into Swindon, Armstrong began looking into the working conditions of the men and their living comfort in the neighbourhood. At his direction ventilation, lighting, and cleanliness were improved in the shops, and measures were taken to save labour and give greater comfort and safety. As a result of his interest in local affairs it became traditional for officials and employees at the Works to take an active part in the management of the town, to look after the general welfare of Great Western families, and to act as magistrates when called upon. Officials at the Works became members of the New Town Local Board. Later on G. J. Churchward joined them, and when the New Swindon Urban District Council was established in 1894 he was elected a member and became its Chairman three years later. He was the first Chairman of the Technical Education Committee when it was set up in 1898. In 1900 the New Town and the Old Town were incorporated as a

Borough; Churchward was elected to the Council and then elected as its first Mayor.[10]

Under Joseph Armstrong the Swindon Works were so ably and economically run that the Directors expressed their particular approval. Sir Daniel Gooch, when in 1872 he was voted a sum of 5,000 guineas by the shareholders for his achievement in restoring the fortunes of the Company, presented £1,000 of it to erect and endow a first-aid hospital for the Works. (No doubt he had consulted Armstrong as to how such a sum could best be used.)

The extent of the gauge conversions and consequent demands for standard-gauge locomotives, carriages, and wagons, faced Armstrong with a formidable task. Yet he managed to produce in the various works under his control the whole of the rolling stock needed to replace the broad-gauge stock as it was withdrawn, without having to go to contractors; and this stock was ready for each section of the railway as soon as it was converted.[11]

An immediate task which Armstrong had to tackle was the building of a carriage and wagon works at Swindon. Up till this time the Great Western had obtained its carriages and wagons from private builders, but the Directors had decided that the Company should now build its own. Gooch had stopped Potter's plan for a carriage works at Oxford, and it was intended that the new works should be at Swindon. Armstrong set about building them on the south side of the main line, and arranged that in the meantime the old Shrewsbury Companies' Saltney Works at Chester and the old West Midland Railway's Works at Worcester should be used for carriage construction.

In 1866 Joseph Armstrong produced the first twelve of his famous standard goods 0–6–0 engines; followed during the next year by more, which were identical except that the outside frames had no ties between the horns. All the subsequent engines had this modification, and by 1877 the class numbered 310 engines. For express passenger traffic Armstrong designed the *Sir Daniel* class of 2–2–2 locomotives with outside frames 7 foot driving wheels, flush-topped firebox, and a dome. Ten more were built in 1866 and another twenty in 1869. They were intended to meet a need for more power on the Paddington–Wolverhampton expresses. At first they had Joseph Armstrong's peculiarly shaped brass safety valve casing, but this was replaced later by the more attractive Beyer Peacock design, in which a large diameter base was connected to a smaller diameter top by a concave curved surface. This pattern was retained throughout the life of the Great Western. The *Sir Daniels* were an

47

immediate success; they had excellent boilers and they ran the majority of the standard-gauge expresses until larger engines supplanted them. Their cylinders and motion were interchangeable with those of Armstrong's standard goods, and in 1899–1901 they were rebuilt by Churchward as o–6–o goods engines (a tribute to their excellent qualities) after they had become too light for passenger duties.[12]

Also in 1866, George Armstrong built at Stafford Road twelve 2–4–0 engines with double frames, domes, flush-topped boilers, and 6 foot coupled wheels for general passenger work. But the most famous of his designs was the o–4–2 tank engine for local passenger trains which Stafford Road began turning out in the same year. The first fifty were saddle tanks, but from 1870 nearly a hundred more were built as side tanks with a longer wheel base, and the original fifty were later rebuilt with side tanks. These engines of the 517 class were in time distributed over the whole of the Great Western system and worked local and branch trains for many years. Ten more were built at Stafford Road in 1895, with outside bearings on the trailing wheels, the year before George Armstrong's retirement; and then Collett built ninety-five more of them in 1932, with some modifications, as the 48xx class, mostly fitted for auto-train working to replace the steam rail motor cars.[13]

In 1868 Joseph Armstrong took William Dean from Wolverhampton and appointed him his Assistant. This, though Dean was only twenty-eight at the time, indicated him as Armstrong's probable successor. With him Dean brought W. H. Stanier (father of Sir William Stanier) as his confidential clerk. (W. H. Stanier was later Stores Superintendent and finished his career as Assistant General Manager of the Great Western Railway. He initiated technical education at Swindon and was responsible for setting up chemical and physical laboratories.)[14]

Joseph Armstrong began building a number of 2–4–0 locomotives in 1868. The first six were the 439 class, with 6 foot 1 inch coupled wheels and inside frames, for stopping passenger trains. They had curved splashers round the rims of the wheels like the broad-gauge engines, and men of the Northern Division nicknamed them the 'Bicycles'. They were followed in 1869 by the 481 class of twenty engines, for the converted South Wales and Weymouth lines, which were very similar but with the more usual type of splasher. In 1871 there were eleven more of the same general pattern—the 717 class. Finally, in 1873, came twenty express 2–4–0s with 6 foot 6½ inch wheels, of which sixteen went to the Neath and New Milford sheds and worked express trains between those towns and Swindon for a number of years.

5   The line of the old South Devon Railway, near Dawlish, in 1939; showing a
Hall class 4–6–0 on an up train. (*British Railways*)

6 The first broad-gaug
passenger train at Redru
West Cornwall Railway,
on 1 March 1867; haule
by SDR *Comet* class 4–4
tank engine, *Lance*, built
in October 1851. Note t
mixed-gauge track.
(*British Railways*)

7 SDR *Leopard* class
broad-gauge 4–4–0 tank
engine *Stag*, built in
December 1872. With h
sister *Leopard*, she was t
last broad-gauge engine
steam, being employed
shunting broad-gauge
carriage stock at Swindo
after the end of the broa
gauge. (*British Railways*)

8 The down *Flying
Dutchman* hauled by 8 fo
single *Eupatoria* passing
Twyford on 14 May 1892
in the last week's working
of the broad gauge. The
train consists of standard-
gauge carriages on broad-
gauge bogies. Note the
arch under construction,
through which now pass
the fast lines. Because it i
being built for the
standard gauge it is not s
wide as the earlier one.
Note also broad- and
standard-gauge lines in t
siding. (*British Railways*)

Other engines that worked South Wales trains were eight old 'singles' which George Armstrong rebuilt in 1872–75. They had been designed originally by Gooch in 1855 and were the first engines ever built by the famous firm of Beyer Peacock.

In 1873 Joseph Armstrong built a notable large 2-2-2, No. 55 *Queen*, and for some years this fine-looking engine with its great polished brass dome hauled the Royal trains. Two years later twenty more engines were built at Swindon which were generally similar to *Queen* but which had domeless boilers. They were known as the *Sir Alexander* class. All these 'singles' had 7 foot driving wheels and, as usual at the time, no cabs.[15]

Joseph Armstrong began the policy of using tank engines for long journeys to save the cost of separate tenders. The elimination of turning was not a factor in this policy because the engines always ran chimney first. They hauled the through coal trains between Newport and Swindon, running at such times that their frequent stops for water did not delay other trains. They were nearly all 0-6-0 saddle tanks, and large numbers were built at both Swindon and Wolverhampton. There were differences, however, between the products of the two Works: the Swindon tanks had double frames, whereas the Wolverhampton engines had single frames and bigger saddle tanks.[16]

Armstrong's engines were simple in design with ample boiler power. His standard-gauge locomotives had 1200 to 1300 ft.^{2} of heating surface, which was considerably more than the 1000 to 1100 ft.^{2} of most other locomotive engineers' designs. He initiated a policy, which Churchward was to follow, of making locomotive parts common to as many classes as possible, so that boilers, cylinders, and other components were interchangeable.[17]

The engines during Joseph Armstrong's time did not have cabs, and the Great Western Railway was, in fact, almost the last of the major companies to fit cabs. Iron-roofed cabs were tried in 1873, but they were not a success and in 1875 a return was made to front weather boards only on the express engines, supplemented in 1876 by side wings. Proper cabs were not provided until 1879, after Dean's succession. Both the Armstrongs had been brought up to drive engines without cabs and they held that in a confined space the fire gave off unhealthy fumes when the regulator was closed—an opinion that was no doubt true of the coke fires usual in their youth.[18] Of course, drivers of horse-drawn vehicles sat (and still sit) in the open, and it was not considered in the early days of the railways that engine drivers needed any greater protection. As trains ran faster, so the weather board with its circular windows was fitted to break the force of wind and rain.

The new Swindon Carriage Works opened early in 1869 and James Holden was transferred from the Saltney Works to become the first Carriage & Works Manager. In March 1870 the Works turned out the first two passenger carriages to be built there—carriages that were also the first on the Great Western standard-gauge lines to have six wheels. During the following year sixty more were built at Swindon, and after these came a large number of both four- and six-wheeled vehicles to replace the broad-gauge carriages on converted lines. In February 1874 the Great Western built a new standard-gauge saloon for Queen Victoria, and she liked it so much better than the old one that she stopped travelling on the broad-gauge track between Windsor and Paddington. This new saloon was the first Great Western standard-gauge passenger carriage with eight wheels.

In January 1876 the Swindon Carriage Works began building new broad-gauge carriages which were badly needed to replace old and run down stock. They included not only six-wheeled vehicles, but also a large number of comfortable and roomy carriages with a four-wheeled truck at each end; though the trucks were not true bogies.[19]

When Churchward arrived at Swindon most of the train services were very slow. During all the time that Joseph Armstrong was in office the Great Western, under Sir Daniel Gooch, had been exercising a rigid economy. There was only one show train, the broad gauge *Flying Dutchman*, and nothing else approached it. When Churchward was completing his last year of pupillage under Joseph Armstrong this famous train was still rolling to a halt at Swindon station behind one of Gooch's 'eight-footers', whilst most of the goods trains were trundling through Swindon hauled by Armstrong's standard goods locomotives, the last of which were still being built in the Swindon Works.

At that time there were separate drawing offices in the Locomotive Works and the Carriage Works, and also in the departments concerned with signals, surveying, construction, and planning. Churchward spent some time in all of these, starting with the locomotive drawing office in 1877. During this period of his career he was at one time on design work in connection with the pumping station at Sudbrook for the Severn tunnel, which was then under construction.[20]

On 5 June 1877 Joseph Armstrong died unexpectedly, to the distress of all those who had known him or who had benefited from his activities on their behalf. On 18 June Gooch wrote in his diary:

'Our railway sustained a great loss on the 5th by the death of our rolling stock engineer, Mr Armstrong. His death was very sudden, he having been only a couple of weeks ill. He has been a very valuable servant to the company, being an able and upright man. I will also feel his loss very much. His department was a very large and important one and my anxiety will not be diminished by having to place it in the hands of a fresh man. We have for some time had Mr Dean in our service as chief assistant to Armstrong with a view of meeting such an event. I hope he will do well. Mr Armstrong was buried at Swindon church on Saturday the 9th in the presence of an immense number of sorrowing people. I and some of the directors went to the funeral and all the officers of the company were there. No man could be more sincerely esteemed.'[21]

Such a lengthy statement in his diary testifies to Gooch's sorrow and sense of loss. It is probable that amongst the mourners who watched Sir Daniel Gooch at the ceremony was Joseph Armstrong's pupil, G. J. Churchward.

Churchward was now to serve a new chief and one who he was himself destined to succeed.

NOTES

1   Robert Young, *Timothy Hackworth and the Locomotive* (London, The Locomotive Publishing Co., 1923), pp. 133*f* and 331*f*.
2   H. Holcroft, *The Armstrongs of the Great Western* (London, Railway World, 1953), pp. 27*f*.
3   Sir Daniel Gooch, *Memoirs and Diary*, ed R. B. Wilson (Newton Abbot, David & Charles, 1972), pp. 3*f*.
4   H. Holcroft, letter to the author.
5   Holcroft, *The Armstrongs*, pp. 28*f*.
6   Ibid., p. 30.
7   Ibid., pp. 31*f*.
8   H. Holcroft, letter to the author.
9   Holcroft, *The Armstrongs*, pp. 49*f*.
10   *The Railway Magazine*, L, p. 96 (January–June 1922).
11   H. Holcroft, 'The Great Western Railway and its Personnel', *The Engineer*, (April 1960).
12   H. Holcroft, *An Outline of Great Western Locomotive Practice* (London, Locomotive Publishing Co., 1957), pp. 25*f*.
     E. L. Ahrons, *Locomotive Working in the Latter Part of the Nineteenth Century*, vol. IV, ed L. L. Asher (Cambridge, W. Heffer & Sons, 1953), pp. 34*f*.
13   H. Holcroft, letter to the author.
14   Holcroft, *The Armstrongs*, p. 65; and letter to the author.

15 Holcroft, *The Armstrongs*, p. 69; and *Great Western Locomotive Practice*, p. 27.
16 E. T. MacDermot, *History of the Great Western Railway*, vol. II, *The Locomotive and Carriage Department* by A. C. W. Lowe (London, Great Western Railway, 1931), p. 545.
17 Ibid., p. 546.
18 Ibid.
19 Ibid., p. 585.
20 H. A. V. Bulleid, *Master Builders of Steam* (London, Ian Allan, 1963), p. 102.
21 Gooch, op. cit., p. 234.

Chapter 4

Brakes and Carriages

This chapter covers the period from 1877–95, during most of which Churchward was concerned primarily with carriages and wagons. From 1887 to 1880 he was working on various tasks in the drawing office; from 1880 to 1882 he was assisting Joseph's son, 'Young Joe', in the design of the vacuum brake; in 1882, at the age of twenty-five, he was for a brief time an Inspecting Engineer for Materials; later in the same year he was appointed Assistant Carriage Works Manager; and in 1885 he succeeded Holden as Carriage Works Manager. He held this appointment until 1895 when he was transferred to the Locomotive Works as Assistant Manager at the age of thirty-eight. He thus spent thirteen years in the Carriage Works, and it must have been slightly frustrating for an engineer who, it would appear, loved steam locomotives.

It was an era of lovely express trains on the Great Western—perhaps the loveliest ever to run in Great Britain. The carriages had elegant clerestory roofs and were painted in a very decorative version of the chocolate and cream livery which had been first adopted on the Great Western in 1864. At the end of the period these carriages were running behind Dean's beautiful 'singles' in their livery of green with Indian red splashers and underframes, enriched with the polished brass of massive dome and other embellishments and with the gleaming copper cap of the chimney. Holcroft, who knew them well, said that they seemed to glide without any noise over the longitudinal sleepers of the old baulk road. These trains were a delight to the eye, but many of them were not very fast. They reflected faithfully the patrician and leisurely tradition of the old broad gauge; but it was not a tradition that Churchward wanted to preserve. He looked forward to powerful locomotives hauling comfortable trains at far higher speeds, and, when the opportunity came his way, he showed his belief that the old conservative ideas could only be swept away by creating an entirely new Great Western image. He had been brought up and trained in South Devon and Cornwall amidst plain

53

brown carriages with plain roofs and austere domeless locomotives with exposed wheels, and to these he returned. Away went chocolate and cream, Indian red splashers, brass domes and (at least partially) copper-capped chimneys. In response to adverse criticism there was an alleged (but typical) Churchwardian retort that he did not care if the outsides of the carriages were tarred as long as the insides were comfortable. Such was the revolution that was in due course to be effected by the young man who in 1880 made his advancement certain by his part in the design of the vacuum brake.

The equipment of trains with continuous brakes had exercised the minds of railway engineers for many years before they came into use. As locomotives were developed in power and speed, so, with the inadequate brakes of the time, it became ever more difficult to bring express trains to a halt within a reasonable distance. Many accidents happened as a result, particularly in the days before the electric telegraph when trains were dispatched by time intervals, and the first indication that a driver might have of the breakdown of a preceding train was the sight of it on the track ahead. The combined efforts of the driver, with his brake on the engine, and of the two or three guards with theirs on the 'brake-compos' could not bring a fast and heavy express train to a halt in less than a half to three quarters of a mile. The electric telegraph and block system of working brought an immense improvement in railway safety, but it was essential that a driver should have at his command brakes sufficiently powerful to enable him to obey the instructions of a signal.

The first proposal to equip trains with continuous brakes seems to have been made in 1857 (the year of Churchward's birth) by James Harris, who had patented a system of working such a brake by compressed air. In 1860 a patent for a vacuum-operated brake was obtained by du Tremblay and Martin of Rouen. A steam ejector was fitted on the engine connected to a pipe which ran along the underside of the carriages, coupled to the top of a brake cylinder under each carriage. Towards the bottom of this cylinder was a diaphragm which had a piston rod connected to its centre. When the ejector was opened the steam drove the air out of the pipe and the upper part of the cylinders; thus creating a vacuum which caused the diaphragm to rise, pulling up the piston and applying the brake.[1] This advanced system got little encouragement in the United Kingdom. The Great Western tried and rejected Clarke's chain brake, which, improved by Webb, was later adopted by the London & North Western and North London Railways.

In 1872 the Board of Trade urged all railway companies to adopt continuous brakes, as well as other safety measures. Replying for the Great Western, Sir Daniel Gooch said that no satisfactory system had yet been invented, and that if one was discovered his Company would be prepared to adopt it.

The Great Western's first trials were with Smith's Vacuum Brake, which had the disadvantage of not being automatic. But in 1876, after brake trials on the Midland Railway during the previous year, the Company fitted Sanders' Automatic Brake experimentally on a standard-gauge train. This train ran daily for many months between Swindon and Taunton. The brake was then improved, and under the name of Sanders-Bolitho it earned a favourable report from the Board of Trade after trials between Didcot and Swindon in March 1878.[2]

In 1880 Dean decided that the Great Western should have its own automatic brake, and that the weaknesses and difficulties of operation in existing systems should be eliminated in its design. The task was given to Joe Armstrong and Churchward. The brake that resulted from their joint efforts remained in use by the Great Western with some modifications for the whole of its separate existence, and its success is a tribute to the genius of Armstrong and the ability of Churchward. How much was due to the ideas of the former and how much to the practical suggestions of the latter it is now impossible to determine. Joe Armstrong died young in tragic circumstances and Churchward, with characteristic modesty, gave him all the credit.

It is not intended to give a full description of the brake, and the following is merely a brief outline of how it worked. Great Western locomotives had already been fitted with powerful steam brakes and initially, therefore, only the carriage stock was to be provided with brake cylinders. Each vehicle had a brake cylinder, and a through length of iron piping with a flexible connection at each end (by which continuity was established between the engine in front and the brake van at the rear). On the tender was a through iron pipe with flexible connections to the leading vehicle at one end and to the locomotive at the other. On the locomotive iron piping extended to the front buffer beam with a flexible connection for use when it was running tender first. On the left side of the engine was a reciprocating pump, driven by the crosshead, to maintain the vacuum in the entire pipe line of the train whilst it was running. From a 'tee' connection to this pipe line below the footplate, a vertical pipe led to a fitting under the driver's control. This fitting was bolted to a facing on the firebox back plate towards the right-hand side, and a supply of dry steam was brought to it by a small internal pipe. The

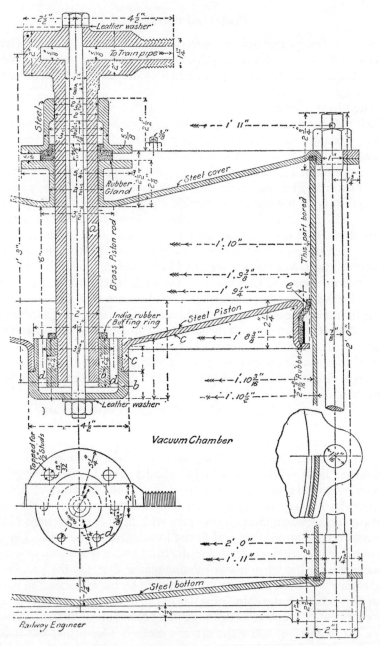

Figure 1 The Armstrong and Churchward vacuum brake cylinder. (*Sidney Stone, 'Railway Carriages and Wagons'*)

56

driver operated the brake by a handle which worked between stops on a quadrant, the spindle to which it was attached being horizontal and at right angles to the back plate. The handle was normally vertical; a movement to the right applied both steam and vacuum brakes simultaneously, moving it to the left released the vacuum brake by admitting steam to the ejector at the back of the fitting, and restoring it to the vertical released the steam brakes by allowing them to discharge through the ejector. The combining cone of the ejector was connected to a long through pipe which carried its exhaust to the smokebox tube plate and thence to the chimney.

The vacuum brake cylinder on the carriages was of unusual design. The end of its piston rod was carried in bearings fixed to the underframe and was free to swing. The piston rod was hollow and was connected to the brake pipe, giving the latter access to the portion of the brake cylinder above the piston. The lower part of the cylinder was extended downward to constitute a reservoir for the vacuum and was not connected to the train pipe. The piston packing was a rubber band that acted as a simple valve to allow air to be withdrawn from the vacuum chamber below the piston, but prevented its return. The bottom of the cylinder was attached to arms of the brake shaft, and when air was admitted to the top of the cylinder, through the train pipe, the cylinder rose on the piston rod, sliding on the piston rod gland, on account of the vacuum below the piston, and brought the brake blocks up to the wheels.

When the vacuum above the piston was restored, the weight of the cylinder itself was sufficient to keep the brake blocks clear of the wheels, so avoiding the need for a spring.

In 1903 the more orthodox arrangement of cylinder was adopted by which the piston rod was connected to the brake shaft and moved to apply the brakes, whilst the cylinder remained stationary.[3]

The work on the vacuum brake was completed in 1882, and Churchward was then appointed an Inspecting Engineer for Materials. This, however, was only an interim job, for he was marked for promotion. A few months later in the same year Dean made him Assistant Carriage Works Manager, with James Holden as his immediate chief.

It was an interesting period in the Carriage Works for the broad gauge was coming to an end and arrangements had to be made, not only for the current requirements on both broad and narrow gauge, but also for the conversion of the broad-gauge carriages to narrow, i.e. standard, gauge in due course. There were three main types of convertible carriage. The earliest were built between 1879 and 1883, and were very handsome

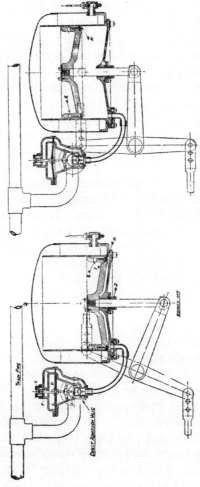

Figure 2 The 1903 pattern vacuum brake cylinder. (*C. H. Mathers, 'The Vacuum Brake', Wilding & Son Limited*)

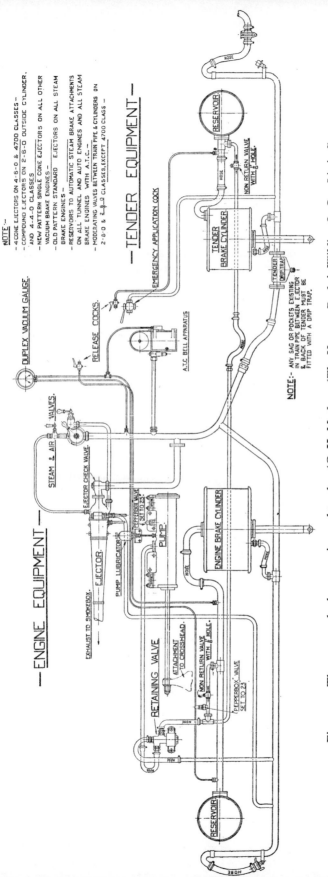

Figure 3 The vacuum brake on engine and tender. (*C. H. Mathers, 'The Vacuum Brake', Wilding & Son Limited*)

clerestory vehicles mounted on 2 four-wheel trucks. Holden had them constructed with a detachable longitudinal portion 1 foot 6 inches wide, and of a height which, after conversion, would suit the loading gauge of the Great Western's standard gauge lines. To convert the carriages the centre portion was removed and the two sides brought together. At the same time the transverse members of the underframe were cut to enable the solebars to be closed up. The next lot of carriages had narrow, or standard, gauge bodies mounted on broad gauge underframes; the vacant space between body and frame along the sides being filled in with a box-shaped platform. The earlier carriages of this type were also mounted on 2 four-wheel trucks, but those built after 1888 had Dean's suspension bogies. By this year Churchward was Carriage Works Manager, for he had succeeded Holden on the latter's departure to become Locomotive Superintendent of the Great Eastern Railway in 1885, so that he may well have had something to do with the change. To convert these carriages the body was lifted and the underframe dealt with in the same manner as for the earlier type. These two classes of carriage supplied the stock for most of the broad gauge expresses during their last years.[4]

The last type of convertibles were modern narrow, i.e. standard, gauge carriages with broad-gauge bogies. They had clerestory roofs and oil gas lighting, and had been designed for express trains on the narrow gauge. It was not worth building similar vehicles for the broad gauge, but it was decided that the principal broad-gauge expresses should have the benefit of the latest improvements in design. In order that conversion should be rapid a number of these carriages were mounted on specially constructed broad-gauge bogies. To convert these carriages from narrow to broad gauge, Churchward made special arrangements in the Carriage Works. Two roads were fitted with hydraulically operated drop tables, so positioned that there was a table under each bogie of a coach. A trestle was brought in at the end of the coach to support the body and its underframe at the buffer cases. After the nuts had been removed from the four scroll irons, the bogie was lowered clear, transversed laterally below the floor level, and brought up again on the parallel road. The narrow-gauge bogies were then rolled away and replaced on the drop tables by broad-gauge ones. When the carriages were restored to narrow gauge the process was reversed. The whole change-over only took half an hour and Swindon could deal with twenty carriages a day.[5]

Non-main-line broad-gauge carriages were not suitable for conversion. They could be found on local trains and on branch lines all over

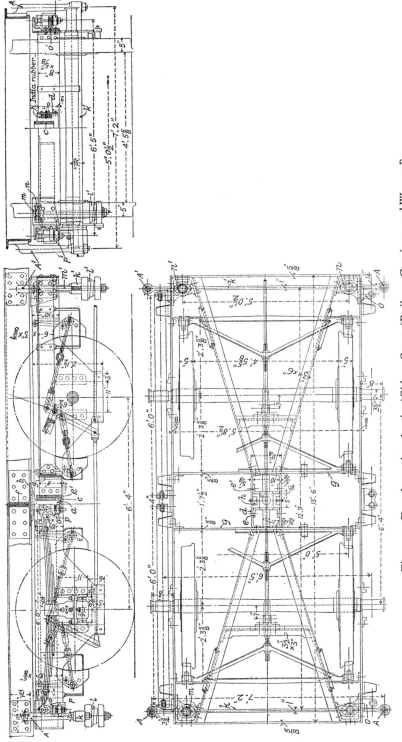

Figure 4 Dean's carriage bogie. (*Sidney Stone, 'Railway Carriages and Wagons'*)

Devon and Cornwall, and they included a large number of weird and archaic specimens. Ahrons says[6] that they 'had to be seen to be properly appreciated. They were utterly unlike anything else on wheels, except perhaps some of the choicest South Eastern specimens of that date'.

The Dean suspension bogie mentioned above was a notable design, How much was due to Dean and how much to Churchward is not known. The general idea was probably Dean's, but it is very likely that Churchward was mainly responsible for its practical application. In its original form the weight of the body and underframe was taken at the four corners of the bogie by vertical suspension bolts, one at each corner. To transmit the weight four scroll irons, or hanger brackets, were riveted

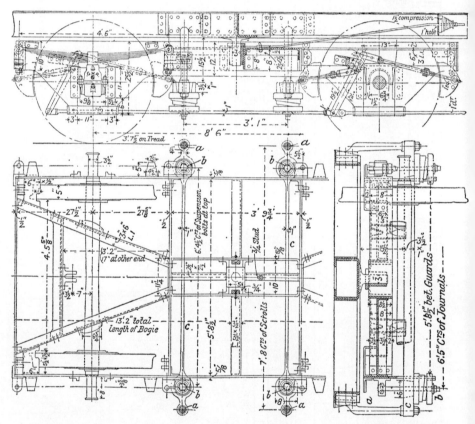

Figure 5 Dean's bogie with inside suspension. (*Sidney Stone, 'Railway Carriages and Wagons'*)

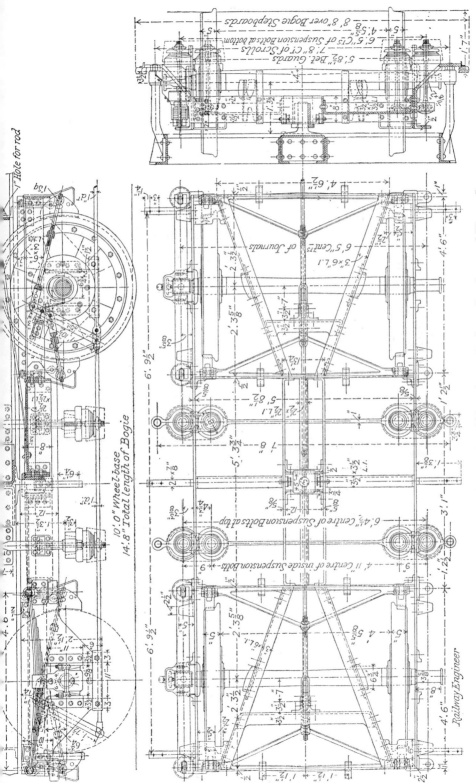

Figure 6 Dean's 10 foot bogie. (Sidney Stone, 'Railway Carriages and Wagons')

to the sides of the solebars, and each pair, i.e. front and rear, carried a cross bar with slots for the suspension bolts to pass through and terminate below volute springs with adjusting nuts. The head of each bolt had a case-hardened washer, spherical on its upper side to engage a corresponding case-hardened washer, carried on each corner of the bogie frame and counter-sunk on its under side. The bogie as a whole swung on these bolts. The bogie frame was of plate which was extended downwards to embrace the four axle boxes. The weight of both body and bogie was taken upon four side springs, each of 6 foot span. The bogie centre pin was riveted by its base to a cross bearer on the underframe and fitted into a block on the bogie frame. The block was free to move laterally one inch on each side, but it carried no weight as there was a good clearance above it. These bogies were fitted with Churchward's 'O.K.' axleboxes and were suited for coach bodies of 52-feet length.

This bogie was developed further in 1892 to carry 56 foot bodies. The wheel base was increased from the original 6 feet 4 inches to 8 feet 6 inches and the scroll irons and cross bars were brought inside the wheel base, while the span of the laminated springs was reduced to 4 feet 6 inches. In 1895 a bogie with a 10 foot wheel base was developed for heavy stock, such as dining cars; it had suspension bolts in pairs, making a total of eight. All these bogies were self-aligning and gave a very comfortable ride, even at the highest speeds.[7]

The 'O.K.' axlebox was due entirely to Churchward. Up till this time grease-lubricated axleboxes had been universal for freight. According to Ahrons,[8] crows were very fond of grease. He had noticed that they could often be seen flying across the front of the engine and asked the drivers with whom he was firing about it. They said that the crow was after the grease and oil, 'and implied that a crow would sell his soul for railway grease.' Ahrons continues that he did not think that the crow fared so well any longer because 'wagon axleboxes, which used to be filled from the top with what was to him that great delicacy yellow grease, are now provided with totally enclosed oil wells with sponge pads'. These were the Churchward O.K. axleboxes.

The grease axleboxes gave little trouble while running at speeds up to 30 m.p.h. or a little over, but were liable to overheat when running any faster. Overheating of axleboxes on carriages was fairly frequent, and in their reports inspectors always gave dirt on the bearings as the reason. Churchward did not accept this because he was convinced that the trouble arose through the failure of the lubrication film, so that metals were in direct contact.

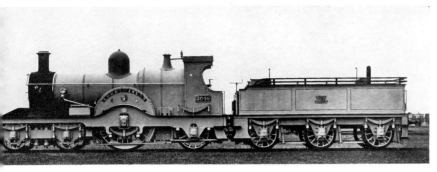

9 *Achilles* class 7 foot 8 inch 'single' express engine No. 3046 *Lord of the Isles*. (*British Railways*)

10 *Duke* class 4–4–0 No. 3258 *King Arthur* as originally built with bogie and tender wheels of Mansell pattern with wood centres (*British Railways*)

11 *Duke* class 4–4–0 No. 3272 *Amyas* with normal bogie and tender wheels, in place of the Mansell pattern. (*British Railways*)

12 The down 10.45 a.m. Paddington to South Wales express passing Swindon without stopping, on 1 October 1895, after the abolition on this day of the compulsory refreshment room stop. The engine is a 4–4–0 of the No. 7 or *Armstrong* class. (*British Railways*)

13 A down train of Dean clerestory carriages hauled by an *Achilles* 4-2-2 passing the Twyford up signal box (now demolished). (*British Railways*)

14 26 June 1898. The 10.30 a.m. express from Paddington to Torquay at Swindon. The train, of clerestory corridor coaches, is hauled by an *Achilles* 4-2-2, and a similar engine waits at the platform on the right. (*British Railways*)

15 6 September 1898. The Swansea to Paddington express at Corsham. (*British Railways*)

16 No. 3048 *Majestic* near Bath on the 10.35 a.m. Paddington to Penzance express on 10 August 1899. (The second portion of the *Cornishman*.) (*British Railways*)

The principal feature of the O.K. axlebox, which he designed, was a patented spring-borne metal-framed pad of horsehair mixed with wool, and braided over with long threads of worsted. The top part bore against the journal and the threads dipped into the oil reservoir. The object of the horsehair was to keep the worsted 'open' so that it would not clog.

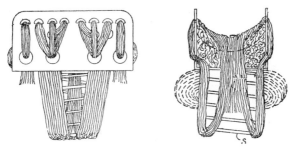

Figure 7 Churchward's axlebox lubricating pad. (*Sidney Stone, 'Railway Carriages and Wagons'*)

The axlebox itself was in two parts, with grooves at the faces; the jointing material being a leather strip. In the bottom of the axlebox was an oil reservoir, and the function of the grooves was to direct any seepage of oil to the reservoir. In the top portion was a supplementary oil chamber above the bearing, so that additional oil could be supplied quickly to the bearing in the event of a hot box. A loose trimming of worsted was put in this oil chamber with one end down an oil way leading to the journal, and by removing a set screw in the top of the axle box the chamber could be filled with oil and the journal lubricated entirely from the top. This was a useful facility should the pad have been damaged by the heating of the journal. The bottom part of the box could be detached quickly for examination of the pad.[9]

To prove his point that dirt in the bearings did not cause hot boxes, Churchward took a brake van out of service. He had a hole drilled through the floor and the corner of the axlebox, through which he inserted a copper pipe with a funnel at the top. The van was attached to a train from Swindon to London, and during the journey Churchward fed emery flour down the funnel. On arrival at Paddington he told the inspectors to feel the box. To their astonishment it was cool; though the journal had a pronounced waist![10]

Another Churchward design of this period was the Great Western pattern of 'either-side' hand brake. The Board of Trade required such a brake to be fitted to all modern freight wagons for use in parking a

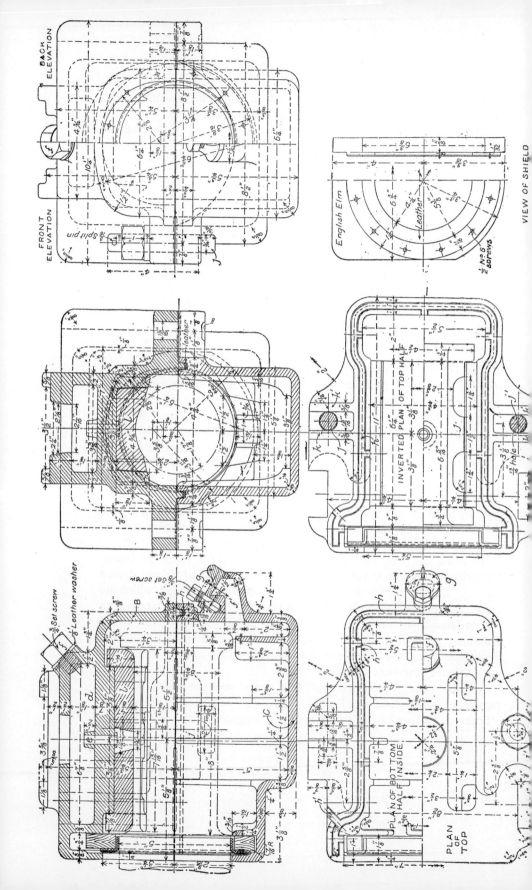

wagon, for regulating its speed by a shunter during fly-shunting operations in sorting sidings, and for assistance in the safe descent of steep inclines. (As regards the last requirement, it was the practice to stop a train not fitted with continuous brakes at the top of an incline to enable the guard to pin down a certain proportion of wagon hand brakes.) The Churchward brake (or more properly the Dean & Churchward brake) complied with the Board of Trade specification that it should be capable of being applied or released from either side of the wagon, that the levers should be of similar pattern on both sides, and that the method of operating both levers should be identical. The levers had a 'press-down' and 'lift-up' motion and a stop when in the off position; they could be operated by one hand and were to the right of the operator when facing the wagon side; and they gave a clear indication as to whether the brakes were on or off.[11]

A notable event during Churchward's time as Carriage Works Manager was the building during 1890–91 of the first British corridor train. It consisted of four carriages and a bogie van and had side corridors with corridor connection between all the coaches. This train, with accommodation for all three classes, entered service between Paddington and Birkenhead on 7 March 1892. The train was steam-heated throughout and the corridor connections were at the sides of the coach ends instead of being placed centrally.[12]

The success of this first corridor train led to a large number of corridor carriages being ordered in February 1893. Corridor connections at the sides of the coach ends were retained, but the brake seconds and thirds vans, which were marshalled at the front and rear of trains, had blank ends. Quarter lights were retained along the corridor side of carriages, so that it is difficult to tell from a photograph whether a train was corridor or not. The first train to the West to receive these new corridor carriages was the 10.15 *Cornishman* Express from Paddington to Penzance. South Wales, Torquay, and other Penzance expresses followed. All these carriages had the 8 foot 6 inch bogie.

Dining cars were not provided until after Churchward left the Carriage Works. This was because, under an agreement made with the contractors in 1841, all regular trains had to stop at Swindon 'for a reasonable period of about ten minutes' to enable passengers to use the refreshment rooms. It was therefore not worth providing dining cars. Eventually in 1895 the Great Western bought the contractors out—but it cost the Company £100,000. On 1 October 1895 two trains in each direction began running through Swindon at full speed. The first was the

Figure 8 Churchward's axlebox for carriages. (*Sidney Stone, 'Railway Carriages and Wagons'*)

down *Cornishman* and the second was the 10.45 a.m. Paddington to South Wales Express. In the middle of the following year the first three dining cars were put into service.

However, by the time the compulsory stop at Swindon had been abolished, Churchward had already left the Carriage Works. Early in 1895 he was appointed Assistant Locomotive Works Manager, with a view to his taking over from the Works Manager, Samuel Carlton, who was due to retire at the end of the year.

NOTES

1 C. H. Mathers, *The Vacuum Brake* (Shrewsbury, Wilding & Sons, 2nd edn 1948), p. 13.
2 E. T. MacDermot, *History of the Great Western Railway* (London, Great Western Railway Company, 1931), vol. II, pp. 588–9; H. Holcroft, *An Outline of Great Western Locomotive Practice* (London, Locomotive Publishing Co., 1957), p. 56.
3 H. Holcroft, letter to the author.
4 Ibid.; and MacDermot, op. cit., pp. 388–9.
5 Ibid.; and H. Holcroft, letter to the author.
6 E. L. Ahrons, *Locomotive and Train Working in the Latter Part of the Nineteenth Century*, vol. IV, ed L. L. Asher (Cambridge, W. Heffer & Sons, 1953), p. 18.
7 H. Holcroft, letter to the Author; and S. Stone, *Railway Carriages & Wagons*, Part I (London, Railway Engineer, 1900), pp. 128–130.
8 Ahrons, op. cit., pp. 46–7.
9 H. Holcroft, letter to the author; and Stone, op. cit., p. 102.
10 Sir William Stanier, 'George Jackson Churchward, Chief Mechanical Engineer, Great Western Railway', *Transactions of the Newcomen Society*, (1960).
11 H. Holcroft, letter to the author.
12 M. Harris, *Great Western Coaches: 1890–1954* (Newton Abbot, David & Charles, 1966), pp. 41–2.

Chapter 5

The Locomotives of William Dean

The locomotives built during the Locomotive Superintendency of William Dean fall into two categories; those which were wholly of Dean's conception, and those which either showed Churchward's influence in their design or were designed almost entirely by him. We are concerned here with the former category, which included, however, two classes of locomotive that decided the pattern of Churchward's first passenger engines.

William Dean was born on 9 January 1840 and was therefore aged thirty-seven when he became Locomotive, Carriage, and Wagon Superintendent of the Great Western. The appointment entailed some personal difficulty because the forceful George Armstrong, to whom he had previously been assistant, was now serving under him, and George had probably hoped to succeed his brother. Dean, however, avoided any clash by leaving George Armstrong to carry on in charge of the Northern Division in the same semi-independence of Swindon that he had been allowed by his brother. He was to continue to do so for nearly another twenty years.

At Swindon there was no immediate departure from the general design policy of Joseph Armstrong. Indeed, out of the 727 locomotives built at Swindon during the whole of this period a very large proportion were either further batches of Armstrong engines or developments from them. For instance, there were 270 more of Joseph Armstrong's 0–6–0 double frame saddle tanks, as well as a number of his 2–4–0 side tanks for local and branch passenger service. There were, too, batches of 2–4–0 tender engines which were of basic Armstrong design, though having larger wheels. All these boilers had domes, though, rather surprisingly, all Dean's own designs had domeless boilers until 1884.[1]

Dean's boiler fashions changed quite often during this period, though not nearly so radically as they did when Churchward's influence was making itself felt. The first domeless boilers had firebox casings and smokeboxes flush with the boiler clothing; in 1884 domes were placed on the first ring of the boiler barrel; and in 1886 the smokebox was enlarged so that it was no longer flush with the boiler. When wider steel plates became available, Dean took the opportunity to make his boiler barrels with two rings instead of three, and at the same time he enlarged the dome and placed it on the second ring. In 1891 Dean re-introduced the raised round top firebox casing of Gooch's day, fitting it to his 7 foot 8 inch 'singles'.[2]

Dean's first express engines were the 157 class 2–2–2s (Nos 157–66) which were turned out from Swindon in 1878–79. They were theoretical rebuilds of ten engines designed by Gooch and built by Sharp Stewart for the Northern Division in 1861, but it is doubtful if any parts of the original locomotives were retained. They had a domeless boiler with flush top casing and sandwich frames. In their original condition (which they retained till 1886–87), E. L. Ahrons thought them the most handsome express engines ever built. They were very successful in performance and in their earlier years they shared the Paddington–Wolverhampton services with Armstrong's *Sir Alexander* class.[3]

The Great Western retained sandwich frames, long after other companies had discarded them, on account of their considerable mileage of longitudinal sleeper road. Even when the broad gauge was abolished in 1892 this type of track remained on most of the main line to Penzance, and there were sections of it on the South Wales, Birmingham, and Weymouth main lines. Ahrons says[4] that he could testify from personal experience on the footplates of both sandwich and solid plate framed engines that the former ran more smoothly and with less vibration on the longitudinal sleeper road.

The building of engines with sandwich frames ceased about 1889, but some twenty years later, whilst at Wolverhampton, Holcroft was fortunate enough to witness new sandwich frames being made for an engine which was being rebuilt—perhaps the last occasion on which they were made. The metal plates of these frames were about $\frac{1}{2}$ inch thick, and these were marked out by templates and punched to shape in the plating shop. The iron distance pieces used to fix the inner and outer plates about 3 inches apart were placed at points where the completed sandwich frame would be fixed to the brackets of the inside frame of the engine. When the pair of plates had been bolted together, the carpenters fitted slabs of oak into the vacant spaces between the plates and ran auger bits through the wood at the bolt holes. 'Next,' says Holcroft, 'a rivet hearth was brought up, and we all set about pushing red hot bars through the holes to open them out and to char the wood in the vicinity of each bolt to destroy acid which might otherwise corrode them.' The bolts were then driven in and their nuts screwed up, after which the completed frame was ready to be put in place on the engine.[5]

As the 157 class were turned out when G. J. Churchward was in the Swindon drawing office it is conceivable that he may have done some work on them. It was a tribute to their capacity that when the non-stop London–Birmingham expresses were inaugurated in 1898 the 157s, now twenty years old, were used in their operation. No. 165, then the sole remaining one of the class, was withdrawn in 1915—the last 2-2-2 locomotive to haul a train in Great Britain.[6] By that time their open splashers with broad brass bands had been replaced by plain closed splashers, and six of them had been given big brass domes.[7]

Dean's numerous 0-6-0 saddle tanks were intended as general-purpose engines and were widely used for local and branch line trains, both passenger and goods. In addition, Dean followed the policy initiated by Joseph Armstrong of using them to work goods trains over as long distances as their fuel supply allowed, and when traffic conditions permitted the necessary stops for water without delaying other trains.[8] (In his diary of 11 September 1778, Sir Daniel Gooch, then staying at Ilfracombe, mentions another type of Great Western branch line motive power. He writes: 'I went in the morning to look at our Great Western stables, as we run coaches from here to Barnstaple.')[9]

Apart, perhaps, from his bogie 'singles', Dean's most famous and successful engines were the 2301 class standard goods 0-6-0s with inside plate frames and 5 foot wheels. The first batch of these were turned out from Swindon in 1883, and there were successive batches from then on till 1898, by which time 280 had been built. Swindon was, of course, still building them when Churchward was Works Manager. Following the Dean boiler fashions; the first twenty were domeless, subsequent batches had domes on the first barrel ring and flush smokeboxes, and the final version had larger smokeboxes and larger domes set on the second barrel ring. In addition, twenty engines of the 2361 series, built in 1885–86, had double frames and underhung bearing springs, for they had been intended for conversion to the broad gauge. In the event, no conversions of this class were needed. In the First World War a large number of these useful little engines were sent for military service in France and in the Mediterranean and Middle East areas. After the war all those still surviving, apart from some which were sold, returned to service on the Great Western. Some twenty years later, on the threshold of the Second World War, the Ministry of Transport announced that if war should occur the War Office would need locomotives for use overseas. It was agreed that as a first instalment to meet this requirement the Great Western Railway should supply 100 0–6–0 goods engines of the 2301 class. These little Dean engines were selected because of their simplicity, their comparatively high power, and their light axle load. To ease the burden on the Great Western, the London Midland & Scottish Railway and the London & North Eastern Railway each agreed to lend that Company forty of their own 0–6–0 locomotives. As their contribution the Southern Railway undertook to help in the preparation of the 2301s for their military service.[10]

The final triumph of the 2301 class came in 1949. A new LMS 2MT class 2–6–0 was sent to the Western Region to be tried in comparison with these now very venerable engines. The drivers reported that the 2301s were better than the 2MT, and this was confirmed by tests carried out at Swindon![11]

Forty double-framed 0–6–0 saddle tank versions of the above engines were built and designated the 1661 class. They were contemporary with the 2361 series of the 0–6–0s and were also intended for conversion to broad gauge if needed.

The provision of engines for the remaining broad-gauge services presented Dean with a problem in the 1880s, because so many broad-gauge engines were becoming worn out that there was a considerable shortage. It was not worth building new engines because the broad gauge had only a limited life remaining to it. The solution adopted was to provide narrow-gauge engines adapted to run on the broad gauge and easily convertible back to the narrow gauge. Such engines had to be built with frames which were outside for the narrow gauge and inside for the broad gauge. Armstrong had started to meet this need by converting fifteen of his narrow-gauge 0–6–0 saddle tank engines, and Dean converted thirty-five more of them in 1884–88. He also converted twenty of Armstrong's standard goods locomotives, mainly for freight traffic in Devon and Cornwall.

The first convertibles built by Dean were half of an order for twenty 2–4–0 tank engines, which were turned out from Swindon in 1885. They had 5 foot 1 inch coupled wheels, and their boilers, valve gear, and certain other components were common with the 2301 class. The broad-gauge engines had, of course, the coupled wheels outside the double frames, but the leading wheels had outside bearings which were carried in additional frame plates. The ten which were drafted to the broad-gauge lines were considerably more powerful than the 4–4–0 tanks of the South Devon Railway, which had monopolised the traffic west of Newton Abbot for so long. They did not replace the South Devon engines but they shared with them the working of the principal trains. When in 1890 the *Cornishman* express was introduced, there was for the first time a non-stop run between Exeter and Plymouth, and the tank engines did not carry enough water for the task. Three of the new locomotives were therefore converted to 2–4–0 tender engines, and they were the first passenger tender engines to work west of Newton Abbot. When they were converted to narrow gauge they resembled the double framed 2361 batch of the 2301 class, except for their wheel arrangement.[12]

In 1887–89 forty 0–4–2 tank engines with 5 foot wheels and sandwich frames were built at Swindon. This was an innovation, because up till then tank engines of this wheel formation had only been built at Wolverhampton, whilst Swindon's four-coupled tank engines had all been 2–4–0s. The first twenty of these locomotives were sent to London to work standard-gauge local services. The other twenty were built as broad-gauge convertibles and, whilst the standard-gauge engines had side tanks, those for the broad gauge had the customary saddle tanks. They were not a success on either the broad or the narrow gauge. The trailing wheels were widely separated from the coupled wheels and had a certain amount of side play—an arrangement which resulted in very unsteady riding. In an endeavour to correct it, the last engine of the broad-gauge batch was given short side tanks, an additional tank in the coal bunker, and a Dean suspension bogie instead of the trailing axle. This effected some improvement and the rest of the class were similarly modified. Nevertheless, they were still subject to derailment when running fast, and eventually they were all completely rebuilt as mixed traffic 4–4–0 tender engines.[13]

Dean's several classes of 2–4–0 tender engines were intended for secondary main line trains and for the principal passenger services on the Weymouth and South Wales lines. The twenty engines of the 2201 class built in 1881–82 were for express service and had 6 foot 6 inch coupled wheels, inside frames and domeless boilers; the boilers of the second ten being rather bigger than those of the first. In 1887–89 Swindon turned out another eighteen of this type to replace Armstrong's 481 class, taking the same numbers. Of these, No. 488 was the first standard-gauge engine to run west from Exeter. She was used to test the track from Exeter to Newton Abbot, after its conversion to standard gauge, on the afternoon of 21 May 1892. The North and West express service, which was started in 1888, was often worked by engines of this class.

The twenty 2–4–0s of the 3206 class, built in 1889, were the last Great Western engines built with sandwich frames. They had 6 foot 1 inch coupled wheels and were intended for mixed traffic duties, and as convertibles if required. They acquired the nickname of the 'Barnums' because, as they could run over most routes and could pull well, they were used at one time to haul the heavy rolling stock of American pattern which had been specially built to carry 'Barnum & Bailey's Great Circus & Menagerie' from one town to another.[14]

The last class of 2–4–0s were the 3232 class of twenty engines which appeared in 1892–93. They were similar to the 2201 class, but had bigger boilers and cylinders. They frequently worked the Shrewsbury–Bristol trains running through the Severn tunnel.

There now follows the Dean foundation on which Churchward was to build, and it comprised two types of express engine—one a 'single' and the other with four wheels coupled.

In 1881 a 4–2–4 side tank locomotive with 7 foot 8 inch driving wheels and inside bearings was built at Swindon. It was somewhat unusual in appearance, for Stephenson's valve gear was placed outside the driving wheels and rocking shafts transmitted the motion to slide valves above the cylinders. It proved a complete failure, doing no useful work and being very prone to derailment. It was soon withdrawn and put quietly away for further thought. Then in 1884 parts of it were used to build a 2–2–2 tender engine, No. 9, and in this the 7 foot 8 inch driving wheels, the outside valve motion, and the rocking shaft drive to the slide valves above the cylinders were all retained. Thus the big eccentrics, rotating outside the driving wheels, distinguished it to the observer from any other 'single' on the line. The boiler was flush topped and the large dome was mounted on the first ring.

In 1886 Dean built another 2–2–2, No. 10, also with 7 foot 8 inch driving wheels, flush-topped boiler, and brass dome on the first ring; but this engine was far more orthodox in appearance though it too had an unusual feature, for the valves were below the cylinders and were driven directly by the link motion. This system had been devised by Stroudley on the London Brighton & South Coast Railway. Holden, when he left the Great Western to become Locomotive Superintendent of the Great Eastern, adopted it on locomotives he designed for the latter railway, and he may well have persuaded his former chief as to its merits. No. 10 has an important place in locomotive history because it became the prototype of Dean's famous 'singles' and thus the ancestor of his 4–4–0s. Nos 9 and 10 were both rebuilt at Swindon in 1890 with driving wheels reduced to 7 foot, outside frames, and valves below the cylinders. In their new guise they were named *Victoria* and *Albert*, respectively. Holcroft saw them when they came to Wolverhampton for repairs and remembers particularly the reversing gear, which was a combination of lever and screw—the former for notching up quickly and the latter for fine adjustment.[15]

As a result of experience with Nos 9 and 10, the 3001 class of thirty 2–2–2 engines was built in 1891–92. On these the driving wheels were restored to 7 feet 8 inches, the boiler had a raised round firebox casing and raised smokebox, the large brass dome was on the second ring, and there were double plate frames and underhung bearing springs to make the engines convertible to the broad gauge. The 3001s were an enlarged version of No. 10 and their primary purpose was to take the place of the broad-gauge eight foot 'singles' on the route to Newton Abbot after it had been converted. The first eight, Nos 3021–28, were built to run on the broad gauge and supplement the *Iron Dukes* on the West of England expresses, but they did not work long over the old Brunel road, for it had gone the following year.[16]

On 16 December 1893 No. 3021 (re-converted to standard gauge) was derailed in Box tunnel owing to a broken leading axle. It appeared that, like the old broad-gauge *Great Western*, the new 'singles' were too heavy at the front end and were unsteady at speed. Between March and September 1894, therefore, the frames of all thirty engines were lengthened and the leading axle was replaced by a bogie. The conventional type with a centre pin on a stretcher between the frames, was ruled out because, with the Stroudley arrangement of the valves, it would have been very difficult to remove the steam-chest covers to obtain access to the port faces below the cylinders. Dean therefore adopted a modification of his carriage bogie. Whether by accident or design, the rebuild produced a locomotive which many (excluding of course Ahrons) considered the most beautiful ever to have run anywhere. It would seem, too, that the superb lines of these engines encouraged their adornment in colour, in polished brass and copper, and in the heraldic embellishment of arms and crests. The original thirty engines were followed, from March 1894 to March 1899, by another fifty, but these were built with bogies from the start. The first thirty of these were completed by April 1895; but there was then a gap of two years before the last twenty began to appear from May 1897, when Churchward was Locomotive Works

Manager at Swindon. Apart from occasional visits to South Wales, most of these eighty bogie 'singles' were confined to the West of England expresses between Paddington and Newton Abbot; and perhaps the railways of the world have offered no more beautiful sight than one of them at the head of a chocolate and cream train of Dean's clerestory coaches. No. 3048 was allocated to Stafford Road shed for the London trains via Leamington, and there was some working via Worcester as well. With the provision of water troughs at Goring and Foxes Wood (near Bristol) the single wheelers ran non-stop from Paddington to Exeter and from Paddington to Newport via the Severn tunnel. As the supplies of water were softened in each case the condition of the London-based engines was much improved.[17]

The other part of this story starts in an unlikely way with two dreadful 2–4–0 compounds, Nos 7 and 8, built in 1886; No. 7 for the standard gauge and No. 8 a convertible built as a broad-gauge engine. No. 7 was inconspicuously awful for a short time and was hastily withdrawn. No. 8's departure from active service was much more dramatic, for on two occasions she broke three of her four pistons and cylinder covers in pieces, and then left the scene, having performed less useful work than perhaps any other locomotive in British railway history. Two years later, in 1888, two more 2–4–0s, Nos 14 and 16, were built at Swindon. These were simple expansion convertibles intended specifically for working the heavy West of England broad-gauge express which left Bristol at 3 p.m. and which nearly always required assistance between there and Swindon. They had 7 foot coupled wheels and sandwich frames. It does not appear that they were ever converted to standard gauge. They had a very short life of only four years, though during that time they were the largest coupled engines on the Great Western.[18]

In 1894 four 4–4–0 express locomotives, Nos 7, 8, 14, and 16, were turned out from Swindon Works. They were nominally rebuilds of the four 2–4–0s discussed above, but they probably incorporated nothing more than the wheels of the engines they replaced. They had the same bogie, boiler, and double frames as the 3001 class 'singles', but they were rather over-cylindered and never did as well as the 4–2–2s. During the 1890s they generally worked the South Wales expresses between London and Bristol. Like the 'singles' they were extremely handsome engines and they were historically important because they set the pattern of development for all subsequent Great Western inside cylinder 4–4–0s. Eventually they were rebuilt between 1915 and 1923 and incorporated in the *Flower* class.[19]

76

Thus the successful bogie 'singles' led to the construction of bogie-coupled express engines, which in turn started the development that culminated in Churchward's *Cities*—the fastest express engines in Great Britain at the time.

NOTES

1   H. Holcroft, *An Outline of Great Western Locomotive Practice* (London, Locomotive Publishing Co., 1957), pp. 45f.
2   Ibid.
3   Ibid.; and E. L. Ahrons, *Locomotive and Train Working in the Latter Part of the Nineteenth Century*, ed L. L. Asher (Cambridge, W. Heffer & Sons, 1953), vol. IV, p. 37.
4   E. L. Ahrons, *The British Steam Locomotive* (London, The Locomotive Publishing Co., 1927), pp. 47, 113.
5   H. Holcroft, *Locomotive Adventure* (London, Ian Allan), p. 33.
6   Holcroft, *An Outline of Great Western Locomotive Practice*, pp. 45f.
7   Ahrons, *Locomotive and Train Working*, p. 37.
8   Holcroft, *An Outline of Great Western Locomotive Practice*, pp. 45f.
9   Sir Daniel Gooch, *Memoirs and Diary*, ed R. B. Wilson (Newton Abbot, David & Charles, 1972), p. 261.
10 Holcroft, *An Outline of Great Western Locomotive Practice*, pp. 45f.
    Colonel H. C. B. Rogers, *The Last Steam Locomotive Engineer: R. A. Riddles* (London, George Allen & Unwin), pp. 106, 172.
11 Ibid.
12 Holcroft, *An Outline of Great Western Locomotive Practice*, pp. 45f.
13 Ibid.
14 Ibid.
15 Ibid., p. 62.
16 Holcroft, op. cit., pp 62–3 and letter to the author; H. M. Le Fleming, *The Locomotives of the Great Western Railway*, Part 7 *Dean's Larger Tender Engines* (RCTS 1954), p. G7.
17 Ibid., p. G10; and H. Holcroft, letter to the Author.
18 Holcroft, *An Outline of Great Western Locomotive Practice*, p. 61; Ahrons, *Locomotive and Train Working*, p. 25.
19 H. Holcroft, letter to the author; Le Fleming, op. cit., pp. G27–9.

Chapter 6

The Dean/Churchward Locomotives

At the time of Churchward's move to the Locomotive Works the new *Duke of Cornwall* class 4–4–0s were being built, the first of them having been completed in May 1895. In their original form they were, of course, an entirely Dean design and of the same 'family' as the bogie 'singles' and the No. 7 class 4–4–0s. They were intended to complement the work of the 'singles' by hauling the West of England expresses between Newton Abbot and Penzance, and it is interesting that they had the same wheel arrangement, with coupled wheels of approximately the same diameter, as the old South Devon tanks. Although three years had elapsed since the abolition of the broad gauge, this section of the Great Western had only just been brought up to a standard able to take the modest 15-ton axle load of the *Dukes*.

The new engines had frames, bogie, and valve arrangements of the same type as the 4–2–2s, though the bogie and tender wheels were of the Mansell pattern with wood centres. The boiler, however, was based on that of the 2301 class 0–6–0 goods locomotives; but the barrel and firebox were longer, and the round-top firebox casing was flush with the barrel. A new feature was an extended smokebox, which had an American pattern diaphragm plate and netting as a spark arrestor. The cylinders were 18 by 26 inches and the coupled wheels were of 5 foot 7 inch diameter. Forty of these engines had been built by 1897.[1]

Although the numerous 0–6–0 engines designed by Armstrong and Dean were adequate for the majority of Great Western goods trains, they were rather under-powered for the heavy coal trains from South Wales. In 1896, therefore, Dean designed as a prototype a 4–6–0 engine with inside cylinders, double frames, and 4 foot 7½ inch coupled wheels. Reverting to broad-gauge practice, he produced a boiler with a raised round top firebox casing which was 5 foot 10 inch wide over the sides and which allowed for a grate area of 35·4 ft.[2]. To accommodate this, the inside frames had to stop short of the firebox front. The boiler pressure

78

was 165 lb./in.^{2}. The built-up and extended smokebox was similar to that of the *Dukes*. Officially the engine was No. 35, but she was known universally by her nickname of the *Crocodile*. For some years she worked trains from South Wales over the Severn tunnel line to Swindon. However, the engine was the only one of its kind and, as the boiler was not to be renewed, this first Great Western 4–6–0 was scrapped in 1905 after a life of only nine years.[2]

In September 1897 Churchward was appointed Chief Assistant Locomotive Superintendent, in addition to remaining as Locomotive Works Manager. He was now clearly designated as the eventual successor to Dean.

The heaviest trains between London and Bristol were by 1897 becoming a little beyond the capacity of the 'singles', with their limited adhesion. The *Badminton* class of twenty 4–4–0 express locomotives with 6 foot 8½ inch coupled wheels were accordingly designed for the task and were completed at Swindon between December 1897 and January 1899. They were the first engines in which the influence of Churchward is apparent. Drawings incorporating a raised round-top firebox had already been issued, when Churchward had it changed to the Belpaire pattern.[3] At this time, although the Belpaire firebox was quite common on the Continent, it had been little used in Great Britain. Beyer Peacock had built some locomotives with these fireboxes for the Belgian State Railways. Next door to the Beyer Peacock Works were those of the Manchester Sheffield & Lincolnshire Railway, whose locomotive engineers took such an interest in the Belgian engines that Thomas Parker, the Locomotive Superintendent, built for the MSL in 1891 his 9C class 0–6–2 tanks, the first engines on any British railway to be equipped with Belpaire fireboxes. His beautiful 11 class 4–4–0s of 1895 had them too, and they became a standard fitting on the MSLR.[4] Churchward was attracted by the direct system of staying and with the increased steam space and water surface. His own design had a space of 1 foot 11⅝ inches between the crown of the firebox and the outer casing. This was almost immediately increased to 2 feet, which was retained as the standard on all subsequent Swindon Belpaire boilers.[5]

It was in 1898 that the hand of Churchward became really apparent in the locomotives constructed at Swindon. Indeed he was already taking over some of the functions of Locomotive Superintendent, because, as Sir Felix Pole told Holcroft, Dean's mental powers were failing and the Directors established Churchward as 'Regent' with authority to take decisions.[6] Dean was never told this and was allowed to believe that he remained in full control. It says much for Churchward's character and delicacy of feeling that he was able to carry out this difficult task, whilst still treating his nominal chief with the deference to which he was accustomed.

By this time most of Brunel's wooden trestle viaducts, which had been such a feature of the lines in Devon and Cornwall, had been replaced by more solid structures in stone. This made possible the use of heavier engines with larger tenders. In 1898–99 twenty more *Dukes* were built, but with ordinary spoked wheels on bogie and tender, and with thicker tyres on the coupled wheels which increased their diameter to 5 feet 8 inches. Fifteen of these had the flush round-top firebox casings, but four had raised Belpaire fireboxes and a pressure of 180 instead of the original 160 lb./in.[2]. The twentieth engine, though actually the first of the batch to be built, was very different. Named *Bulldog*, it had a much larger boiler and a straight-sided Belpaire firebox, lengthened from 5 feet 10 inches to 7 feet. This large boiler marked a turning point in Great Western locomotive design, for it was the prototype of Churchward's Standard No. 2, though it still retained a dome.[7]

Of the twenty *Badminton* class engines, the nineteenth, *Waterford*, completed three months after *Bulldog*, had the same boiler but without a dome; the safety valves in their brass casing being mounted in the position previously occupied by the dome. The reason for the change was that Churchward had now verified by experiment his belief that steam collected from the top of a flat firebox casing resulted in less priming than when collected from a dome.[8]

In 1899 Churchward followed up Dean's initial essay into solving the South Wales coal traffic problem. The result was another 4–6–0, No. 2601, but of such ugliness that (the Boer War having started) the enginemen nicknamed it *Kruger*. It had double frames, 4 feet 7½ inch coupled wheels, and inside cylinders with a diameter of 19 inches and the unusually long stroke of 28 inches. The boiler was domeless and it had a raised Belpaire firebox casing which was extended to take in a combustion chamber. At its front end the boiler was straddled by a singularly hideous sandbox, which had no facilities for refilling it. The motion had single slide bars and 8½ inch diameter piston valves above the cylinders operated by Stephenson's valve gear through rocking shafts. These piston valves were the first to be used on the Great Western. The boiler pressure was at first 200 lb./in.[2], but this was soon reduced to 180 lb./in[2]. The next engine of the class had a leading pony truck instead of a bogie, because of the satisfactory performance of such a truck on No. 33 (dis-

17   No. 3030 *Westward Ho* near Bath on the 10.20 a.m. Paddington to Falmouth express on 12 August 1899. (*British Railways*)

18   *Bulldog* class 4–4–0 No. 3419 *Evan Llewellyn* as originally built with cast iron chimney and parallel boiler. (*British Railways*)

19   *Bulldog* class No. 3434 (late *Joseph Shaw*) with copper-capped chimney, coned boiler, and top feed. (*British Railways*)

20   4–6–0 No. 100, later *William Dean*. (*British Railways*)

21 Nord Railway
Atlantic No. 2670.
(*Chapelon collection*)

22 *City* class 4–4–0
No. 3434 (later 3711)
City of Birmingham, as
originally built with
coned boiler and cast
iron chimney. (*British
Railways*)

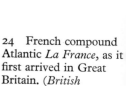

23 *City* class 4–4–0
No. 3433 (later 3710)
City of Bath, with
copper-capped chimney
(*British Railways*)

24 French compound
Atlantic *La France,* as it
first arrived in Great
Britain. (*British
Railways*)

25 No. 102 *La France*
at Bristol Temple
Meads station, suitably
embellished for working
on the Great Western.
(*British Railways*)

cussed below). No. 2602 was almost inevitably *Mrs Kruger*! Eight more of the 2–6–0s were built, making with the 4–6–0 a class of ten. In the last six the boiler pressure was reduced to 165 lb./in.[2]. No. 2602 was built in 1901 and the remainder in 1903. They worked the heavy coal trains between Neath and Swindon with reasonable success; but the boilers (particularly the combustion chambers) gave trouble, the piston valves were poor, and the crank axles were inadequate and had short lives. By 1907 all the *Krugers* had been scrapped. Churchward, in fact, by trying too many innovations had over-reached himself.[9] This is the particular interest of the class, because it was a mistake that Churchward never made again. In all his subsequent development he went step by step, building on his own experience and that of others.

Further development, though, followed quickly. In October 1899, two months before *Kruger*'s appearance, a new 4–4–0 engine, *Camel*, rolled out from Swindon. It was in essence another *Duke*, but the boiler was similar to that of *Waterford*, except that it had a cylindrical smoke-box carried on a saddle built up from the cylinders. Perhaps to the layman the most striking innovation was the replacement of the traditional steel plate chimney with copper top by a plain one of cast iron. *Camel* was the first of a large class of 4–4–0s known as the *Bulldogs*, after the first engine with a Churchward boiler. (*Bulldog* itself later received the *Camel* type boiler, and a number of *Dukes* were rebuilt as *Bulldogs*.) Because of fractures on the earlier engines, the frames were strengthened by giving them straight tops, instead of curves over each axlebox, so that the plate was deepened between the coupled wheels.[10] Most of the *Bulldogs* were sent to reinforce the *Dukes* in Devon and Cornwall and to take over from them the working of the more important expresses west of Newton Abbot.

In 1900 a 4–4–0 named *Atbara*, with 6 foot 8½ inch coupled wheels was built with the same boiler as *Camel*; bearing the same relationship to the *Badmintons* as *Camel* to the *Dukes*. The *Atbaras* also became a large class and were at first put on to the same duties as the *Badmintons*. Later they replaced the bogie 'singles' on the West of England expresses and took over the best South Wales, Wolverhampton, and Shrewsbury via Bristol trains. The *Atbaras* had straight-top frames from the first, and cast iron chimneys similar to those of the *Bulldogs*.[11] A noteworthy feature of the *Atbaras* was the large area of the steam and exhaust ports. The steam ports were 16 by 1¾ inches and the exhaust ports 16 by 3 inches.[12] With 18 inch diameter cylinders this gave a net ratio of port area to piston area of 1:9, at a time when 1:10 was considered good. The

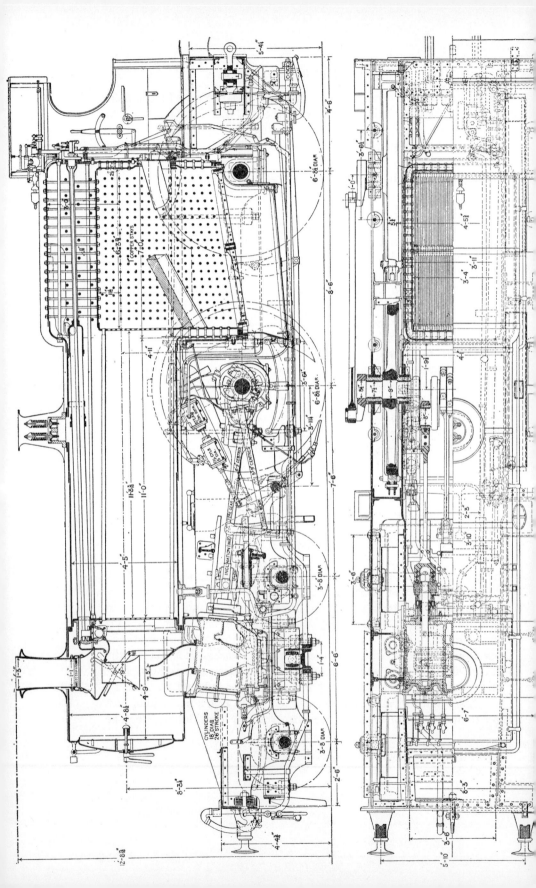

Atbaras, in consequence, were free steaming and fast-running engines. The importance of the steam circuit was thus already engaging Churchward's attention.

At the end of the century, then, the best trains were being worked by locomotives with a typically Dean appearance below the running plate, but with a much more austere appearance above.

Another notable engine of 1900 was No. 33, which was mentioned above. This was a heavy freight locomotive of which the design was based on that of *Atbara* and *Camel.* It had a cast iron chimney, double straight-top frames, and boiler, cylinders, motion, and axles which were common with them. It had a 2–6–0 wheel arrangement, with a leading pony truck and coupled wheels with a diameter of 4 feet $7\frac{1}{2}$ inches. No.33 was most successful and the following year twenty more, known as the *Aberdare* class, were built. Eventually there were eighty-one, and they supplemented and then replaced the *Krugers* on the coal trains.

There were now three classes of engines running with the new type Churchward boiler—the *Bulldogs,* the *Atbaras,* and the *Aberdares.* Great care had been taken in the design of the boiler to eliminate the possibility of priming due to the absence of a dome. When Patrick Stirling fitted domeless boilers to his Great Northern express engines, he avoided the risk of priming by lowering the top of the inner firebox. This reduced the circulation of the water in the boiler; but such a reduction was not acceptable in Great Western engines because they were required to work so much harder. Churchward, to avoid reducing the circulation, increased the distance between the tops of the inner and outer fireboxes by raising the latter.[13] As mentioned above, the distance he selected was 2 feet, and he tried this dimension first on a boiler fitted with a dome before building a domeless boiler. The Standard No. 2 boiler fitted to these three classes was undoubtedly the best in Great Britain at the turn of the century, perhaps in the world.

All three classes retained the double plate frames which had been practically abandoned on all other railways. The coupled axles had bearings in each frame; but the bogies of the 4–4–0s were the Dean suspension type with bearings only in the outside frame, whilst the pony truck of the *Aberdares* had only inside bearings.

The next engine to receive this type of boiler, also in 1900, was No. 11, a 2–4–2 side tank; but the boiler was rather shorter than the *Camel* pattern and was designated the Standard No. 3. No. 11 had inside frames and the same type of piston valves as the *Krugers.* These were solid plug valves with water grooves in the heads instead of packing rings

Figure 9 Atbara class 4–4–0 express locomotive. (*C. E. Wolff, 'Modern Locomotive Practice')*

and they depended on their steam tightness on being a good fit in the liners. In theory they had the minimum frictional resistance, and if a certain amount of live steam leaked past their heads it was considered that this would be less than that consumed in overcoming the friction of the slide valves, which were fitted to all other Great Western locomotives. Other advantages were that the heads were cheap to make and good clear openings were obtained for steam and exhaust. However, in practice the valves were not a success. A slight distortion of the cylinder casting under heat caused scoring between the head and the liner, and the clearance necessary to prevent this scoring led to a greater steam leakage than had been anticipated.[14] Another twenty engines were built with piston valves, but a later batch of 1903 had slide valves, and the earlier engines were so altered when they passed through the shops.[15]

So far nearly all Churchward's designs had been adaptations of Dean's practice; not that he disapproved of this practice, because he went on building double framed inside cylinder 4–4–0s until 1910. But a drawing dated January 1901 shows that he regarded his production of these engines as an interim measure whilst designs for a range of vastly different standard engines were worked out. This drawing gave outline specifications for six projected classes, all with 18 inch by 30 inch outside cylinders and $8\frac{1}{2}$ inch diameter piston valves. Of particular interest in these common dimensions were the remarkably long stroke in the cylinders and the large port openings obtainable with piston valves of this diameter. The six classes comprised two 4–6–0s, one for express work and the other for mixed traffic, a heavy freight 2–8–0, a 4–4–0 for lighter express trains, a 4–4–2 tank for fast short distance trains, and a 2–6–2 mixed traffic tank for suburban and general branch line duties. As many components as possible were common to all. The boilers were of the same pattern except that those for the 4–6–0s and the 2–8–0 had a longer barrel and firebox than those for the other three classes. Coupled wheels for the three express types were all 6 feet $8\frac{1}{2}$ inches, the mixed traffic 4–6–0 and the 2–6–2 tank had 5 foot 8 inch wheels, and for the 2–8–0 they were 4 feet $7\frac{1}{2}$ inches. Radial, pony, and bogie wheels were all 3 feet 3 inches. All these engines were eventually built, though the mixed traffic 4–6–0 did not appear till after Churchward's death.[16]

This plan of 1901 shows not only remarkable foresight but a vision in design that was far ahead of any other locomotive engineer of his day, with the sole possible exception of the Frenchman, Gaston du Bousquet.

The 4–4–0 is perhaps a rather surprising inclusion in the above list, but it was intended primarily for working trains over the Shrewsbury and Hereford line which was owned jointly with the London & North Western Railway. The LNWR had objections to 4–6–0 engines running on this route. Sir William Stanier, in the discussion on the paper presented by K. J. Cook on Churchward's work on the Great Western, said that Churchward was not going to be instructed by Webb (then Locomotive Superintendent of the LNWR) and designed an engine that had plenty of power to run the service but which had a front end admittedly too powerful for the wheel base.[17]

The Swindon Locomotive Works, when Churchward entered them, were ill suited for the building of much larger and more powerful locomotives on the scale that he envisaged. Indeed, he probably regarded them as almost antediluvian. Power was provided by converting to stationary use the main framing, cylinders, and crank axle of an old locomotive. The crank axle, through a large and wide wheel, drove by a belt the main run of shafting in the machine shops, and from this power was transmitted to other parallel rows of shafting. The steam was supplied from specially adapted old broad-gauge locomotive boilers. (The square grate of the broad gauge boilers produced much steadier steaming than did the long narrow grate of the narrow-gauge ones.[18])

Churchward, then, was faced with the enormous task of modernising and expanding the Works; a task that he started almost as soon as he became Locomotive Works Manager.

The power supply was, of course, woefully inadequate, but by 1902 this had been revolutionised. Entirely new and very modern equipment was housed in a building that had been taken over for the purpose because it was suitable for sinking foundation blocks for the generating equipment and had sufficient height to accommodate a travelling crane over the whole plant for erection and servicing. Three generating sets were installed, driven by Westinghouse vertical multicylinder high speed 650 horsepower gas engines, the gas for which came from the gas works by an underground pipe. These engines had electric ignition and a system of mixing gas and air before admission to the engine cylinders, and were governed by throttling this mixture. Associated with the equipment were condensing apparatus and water cooling auxiliaries. From this plant electric power was supplied to the various shops.

An electrically driven compressor was installed in the boiler shop with reservoirs and with piping to various points. By the use of compressed air hammers and drills the speed of repairs was greatly accelerated, with a consequent reduction in cost. These pneumatic tools were also installed in the erecting shop. In the machine shop the larger electrically driven tools, being independent of shafting, could be sited for convenience. Automatic and semi-automatic lathes were concentrated and group driven. In addition, those consuming long bars of round, square, or hexagonal section, though closely spaced, were slightly angled, so that the working of one machine did not interfere with the rest.

Churchward made greater use than before of coal gas for furnaces and for such purposes as expanding tyres by heat for shrinking on to wheel centres. To effect this, retorts and purifying plant at the gas works were enlarged and modernised to incorporate the latest practices, and gas holders of greatly increased capacity were installed.

The scheme for the famous 'A' shop on new ground was begun about 1902, the year of Dean's departure. It covered an area of one and a half acres. There were four sections, all under one roof—the erecting shop, the machine and fitting shop, the boiler shop, and the wheel shop. The erecting shop had two electric traversing tables and four overhead cranes of 50-ton capacity, with electric travelling and hydraulic lifting power. The electrification of the other three shops was by individual drive and by grouping of machines.[19]

The completion of all this work takes us, of course, rather beyond the period covered by this chapter, but it was carried forward on a progressive plan, and at the end Swindon was the best-equipped locomotive works in the country. A remarkable feature was the comparative cheapness with which it was carried out. Making an existing building do for the power house, for instance, saved an enormous amount of money. Holcroft visited it in 1911 and writes: 'My impression of the power house itself was that it was a frowzy place and that it was regarded as being a purely functional conversion. No glamour here; and not the place to exhibit to visitors to the Works. Was not this simple solution of a problem and its lack of publicity typical of Churchward!'[20]

The first engine built entirely to Churchward's ideas was a 4–6–0 express locomotive with inside frames and outside cylinders, which was turned out by Swindon in February 1902, when Dean was still nominally Locomotive Superintendent. Like Churchward's later 'Pacific' engine, it was a prototype, and many of its features were to be improved vastly in its successors (for, unlike the Pacific, there were many). It had the 18 inch by 30 inch cylinders projected in 1901, but the piston valves, probably because of continuing difficulties, were only of $6\frac{1}{2}$ inches in diameter. The motion of these was derived from Stephenson valve gear transmitted through rocking levers. The steam ports were $20\frac{1}{2}$ inches by $1\frac{5}{8}$ inches and the exhaust ports $20\frac{1}{2}$ inches by $2\frac{7}{16}$ inches, which gave a net area of steam passage of about 25 in², or a ratio of port area to piston area of about 1:10. The diameter of the coupled wheels was 6 feet 8½ inches. The boiler had a 9 foot Belpaire firebox with a grate area of 27·62 ft.², and the barrel was domeless with an outside diameter of 5 feet. This was the prototype of Churchward's Standard No. 1 boiler, and it had the then high pressure of 200 lb./in.². It was an enlargement of the *Camel* type, with a raised firebox casing, safety valves on the barrel, and a drum smokebox carried in a saddle. But there was some concession to tradition, for the chimney was steel with a copper top. This engine, No. 100, was later, in honour of Churchward's former chief, named *William Dean*. It was intended as the forerunner of a class to take over the London–Exeter–Plymouth service, for Churchward had recognised that accelerations would be necessary and that more adhesion would be required on heavy trains than a 4–4–0 could provide.[21]

During this period when Churchward had been gradually taking over responsibility there had been little change in the design of carriages. After he left the Carriage Works, corridor carriages, all of the clerestory pattern, were produced in large numbers. Corridor trains were steam heated and restaurant cars had gas cooking. In 1897 some fine sleeping cars appeared, but the most notable production of that year was the corridor Royal train. It consisted of six coaches: full brake with lavatory, attendant's saloon, Queen's saloon, officials' saloon, first class coach, and full brake with lavatory. The Queen's saloon was a rebuild of the earlier one, for the Queen's Secretary had informed the Company that it was her wish that the 1874 saloon should be retained. This had necessitated the removal of the body from the old underframe and its lengthening and remounting on an underframe which matched those of the other vehicles of the train. These were the first Great Western carriages to be fitted with electric light.

In 1900–01 two centre-corridor sets were built for the New Milford boat trains, running in connection with the cross-channel services to the South of Ireland. They were the first trains on the Great Western, in normal service, to have electric lighting and the first to have non-compartment carriages. But this last feature was so unpopular with the travelling public that the Great Western never built other than compartment carriages again.[22]

NOTES

1 H. Holcroft, *An Outline of Great Western Locomotive Practice* (London, Locomotive Publishing Co., 1957), pp. 62f.

2 H. Holcroft, letter to the Author; and Holcroft, op. cit.
   H. M. Le Fleming, *The Locomotives of the Great Western Railway*, Part 7 *Dean's Larger Tender Engines* (RCTS 1954), p. G38.

3 Holcroft, op. cit.

4 George Dow, *Great Central*, vol. II (London, Locomotive Publishing Co., 1962), p 261.

5 K. J. Cook, 'The Late G. J. Churchward's Locomotive Development on the Great Western Railway', *Journal of the Institute of Locomotive Engineers*, Paper No. 492 (March–April 1950).

6 H. Holcroft, letter to the author.

7 Holcroft, op. cit., p. 67; Le Fleming, op. cit., p. G13.

8 G. J. Churchward, *Large Locomotive Boilers* (Institution of Mechanical Engineers, February 1906).

9 Holcroft, op. cit., pp. 74–5, and letter to the author; Le Fleming, op. cit., pp. G39–40.

10 Holcroft, op. cit., pp. 68*f* and letter to the Author.

11 Ibid.

12 E. C. Poultney, *British Express Locomotive Development* (London, George Allen & Unwin, 1952), p. 85.

13 A. Chapelon, letter to the author.

14 H. Holcroft, letter to the author.

15 Ibid.

16 Cook, op. cit.

17 Ibid.

18 H. Holcroft, letter to the author.

19 All the information about the rebuilding of Swindon Locomotive Works was supplied to the author by H. Holcroft.

20 H. Holcroft, letter to the author.

21 A. Chapelon, letter to the author.

22 M. Harris, *Great Western Coaches* (Newton Abbot, David & Charles, 1966), pp. 50*f*.

Chapter 7

The Du Bousquet/De Glehn Atlantics

Before considering Churchward's work after he became Locomotive Superintendent, it is worth outlining the developments in France that led to the remarkable Atlantic locomotives designed jointly by Gaston du Bousquet and Alfred de Glehn; for without these Atlantics, there would not have been (at least, not in the form that we know) any *Stars*, *Castles*, *Kings*, or LMS *Princesses*.

The French story starts, oddly enough, with an erstwhile Great Western man. We last encountered Thomas Russell Crampton as Chief Draughtsman to Daniel Gooch in the very early days of the GWR. He was always of an original and inventive turn of mind, and on 15 February 1842, in conjunction with John Coope Haddan, he took out his first patent. In this there appeared the first hint of the ultimate Crampton system. A year later he had worked out the design for a locomotive in detail and was able to lay his drawings before Gooch for examination and acceptance. It was no accident that he left the Great Western in 1844! The following year he joined that well respected locomotive builder, G. Rennie. Here, perhaps with Rennie's help, he developed his ideas into acceptable locomotives, and in 1848 he set up on his own in London as a civil engineer.[1]

Crampton's aim in locomotive design was to obtain the same speed, stability, and power on the standard gauge as Gooch had achieved with his 8 foot *Iron Dukes* on the broad gauge. To do this he considered that he needed large driving wheels, a big boiler, and a low centre of gravity. To get the low centre of gravity it would be necessary to lower the boiler, and the driving wheels would therefore have to be behind the firebox. But as the weight of the boiler was only about one-third of that of the whole of the locomotive, he did not think he need bother too much over the loss of its contribution to adhesion. To avoid long connecting rods, he brought the cylinders back, close to the longitudinal centre of gravity. This had the advantage, in addition, of eliminating overhang at the front, and, as the position of the driving wheels eliminated it also at the rear, the engine had practically no pitching motion. Some of his engines were domeless, the steam being taken the whole length of the barrel by a pipe placed near its top and pierced with openings on its upper surface. Crampton often used double frames to form a rigid chassis, and he secured the cylinders between them to prevent deformation from the thrust exerted by the piston.[2]

Crampton's first success came in 1845 with an order for two locomotives on his system from the British-owned Namur & Liége Railway. These two, named *Namur* and *Liége*, were built by the little-known firm of Tulk & Ley at Whitehaven. Other orders followed, and in 1848 there came the great 6–2–0 *Liverpool* for the London & North Western Railway, which gained the grand medal of honour at the 1851 Exhibition—to the great disgust of Gooch, whose own *Lord of the Isles* received a lower award. But the *Liverpool* was too heavy for the period; its long rigid wheel base, combined with a weight that was unevenly distributed on the axles, damaged the road, and it was soon withdrawn.[3]

Although thirty-four Crampton locomotives were built for railways in Great Britain, they were not on the whole popular and did not have very long lives. It was far otherwise on the Continent. In France seventy Cramptons were built for the Nord Railway, twenty-seven for the Est, and forty for the PLM. In Germany 135 were bought by fourteen different railways. Most of the German engines lasted into the 1870s and quite a number were running in the 1890s. In France the last Nord Crampton went in 1895, but the Est still had twenty-six in 1902.[4]

The first French Crampton locomotives were put into service on the Paris–Calais line in 1849. They were built in Paris by the Chaillot Works of *Derosne et Cail*. Crampton was assisted in their design by engineers of the French railway and by M. Houel, Chief Engineer of *Derosne et Cail*. The latter took particular care over the detail design. From these combined efforts there emerged a locomotive of excellent proportions, the success of which was assured.[5] It is probable that, as a result of the collaboration by the French engineers, the Nord Cramptons were better than any of the type built in England.

In its large dimensions, the boiler of the Nord Cramptons equalled that of the *Iron Dukes*, but Crampton's valve motion was far better. Stephenson's gear was used with long-travel valves and wide steam passages. The ratio of valve port area to the cross section of the cylinder was 1:8.4, a ratio that was never bettered until Churchward built his two-cylinder 4–6–0 No. 98. The excellent steam circuit was responsible for the great speeds attained by these engines and for their economy in working. Crampton, in fact was so far ahead of his time that the principles initiated by him did not reach their full development until Chapelon rebuilt the Paris–Orleans Pacifics with port to cylinder ratios of 1:4.93 high pressure and 1:7.64 low pressure. The power losses at 60 m.p.h. were approximately the same in the Crampton and the rebuilt Pacific, and $2\frac{1}{2}$ times better than in Stirling's 4–4–2 of 1870.[6]

Lack of adhesion was the principal weakness of the Cramptons. The Nord fixed a lead weight across the footplate and the Est weighted the driving wheels. But in spite of this lack of adhesion, they hauled express trains in France for twenty-five years, and they were particularly economical both in their consumption of fuel and water and in their maintenance.

The Crampton engine had a considerable influence on locomotive design in France, of which one is reminded by the continued French designation of a round top firebox as a *foyer Crampton*. The location of the cylinders near to the longitudinal centre of gravity was excellent, and it was copied in the Est's 500 class of 1878 and the Midi's 1600 class 2–4–0s of 1885. The stability of these engines was far superior to that of the Paris–Orleans and PLM 2–4–2s, which had their cylinders over-hanging in front. On the compounds of du Bousquet and de Glehn this same disposition was retained for the outside cylinders, which were immediately in front of the coupled wheels and driving the second coupled axle. Churchward adopted the same arrangement from the French Atlantics for his four-cylinder engines, so that Crampton's work eventually had its effect on the railway on which he started his career. All subsequent Great Western engines with four cylinders had the same disposition; Stanier took it to the LMS for his *Princess* Pacifics; and Edward Thompson placed the outside cylinders of his three-cylinder Pacifics in similar fashion.[7]

Crampton's influence was even more marked in his use of large steam passages, though this feature of his designs was not at first appreciated. Gaston du Bousquet saw it, realised its vital importance, and embodied a progressively improved steam circuit in his Atlantic and later designs. Alone, apparently, amongst British locomotive engineers, Churchward seized on the importance of the steam circuit at about the same time as du Bousquet. He may have discovered it on his own account, but, having regard to the care with which he studied the work of other engineers, it is quite likely that he too had wondered at the performance of the Crampton locomotives.

The next link in the chain that led to the Great Western four-cylinder engines occurred in 1885. Alfred de Glehn, an Englishman of French descent who was Chief Engineer of the *Société Alsacienne de Constructions Mecaniques*, suggested to du Bousquet, Engineer-in-Chief of Rolling Stock and Motive Power on the Nord Railway (roughly equivalent to Locomotive, Carriage, and Wagon Superintendent), his idea of a four-cylinder compound express locomotive with uncoupled driving wheels (a 2–2–2–0), and with inside high pressure and outside low pressure cylinders driving different axles. This engine, No. 701, was put into service on the Nord in January 1886. Later it was rebuilt with a leading bogie. In 1970 the author saw this venerable ancestor of Churchward's *North Star* being restored in Dunkirk Locomotive Works, and it is now preserved in the railway museum at Mulhouse.

In 1891 there were built for the Nord two engines with four driving wheels and a leading bogie, Nos 2121 and 2122, the first to be designed jointly by du Bousquet and de Glehn incorporating the compound system invented by the latter and applied to No. 701. No. 2122 was a 4–4–0, with its driving wheels coupled, but No. 2121 was a 4–2–2–0 with uncoupled driving wheels, so that comparison could be made between a coupled engine and a 'double single'. As compared with No. 701, the position of the cylinders was reversed, the high pressure being outside and the low pressure inside, with the object of providing a shorter and more direct passage from the latter to the blast pipe. The high pressure cylinders were immediately in front of the leading driving wheels (the position occupied by the low pressure cylinders of No. 701) and drove the second pair of driving wheels, whilst the inside low pressure cylinders were above the bogie and drove the leading driving wheels. This became the classic du Bousquet/de Glehn arrangement. The steam to the rather small steam chests was supplied through vertical pipes running down each side of the boiler and having a large cross-section to prevent undue fluctuations during admission. The firebox was of the Belpaire pattern.[8] To provide extra power at starting, a bypass arrangement allowed the high pressure cylinders to exhaust directly to the atmosphere, so that the engine could be operated as a four-cylinder simple; live steam being admitted to the intermediate receiver which supplied the low pressure cylinders. If necessary the engine could work as a two-cylinder simple, using either the high pressure or the low pressure cylinders, thereby enabling it to keep moving even if partially disabled. Each set of cylinders had its own independently controlled valve gear, so that when working compound the driver could control the admission of steam into the two sets of cylinders by separate adjustment.[9] These two engines put up most impressive performances, No. 2122 running just as freely as No. 2121 and having the advantage of better adhesion. As a result thirty-five more coupled engines were built (Nos 2123–57), though with larger smokeboxes, and No. 2121 was converted to a 4–4–0.

At this time the Midi Railway had excellent relations with the Nord, and in 1893 it ordered fourteen 4–4–0 compound express locomotives which, except for some standard Midi fittings, were identical with the Nord engines. The first two of this Midi 1701 class had a fairly short smokebox like the Nord 2121 and 2122, but the remainder had the longer smokebox fitted to the later Nord engines. The long smokebox was intended to reduce the amount of red-hot cinders thrown out of the chimney when the engine was working hard, on account of the lineside fires from this cause in hot dry weather. The Midi compounds were more powerful and economical than the 1601 class 2–4–0 simple expansion engines that they replaced, but, even so, they had little reserve of power. Midi fuel was poor and their performance never equalled that of their Nord sisters. The Midi, therefore, asked the *Société Alsacienne* to design and build for them some more powerful engines of the same type. This new 1751 class of thirty-four engines was built in 1895–1901. The first of them came into service in 1896 and did so well that in 1897 another of them was tried on the Est and then on the Belgian Etat. The Est liked the trial engine so much that they built twenty-four of the same type and designated them the 2409 class. They were practically identical with the Midi 1751s, though slightly more powerful. The Ouest Railway, meanwhile, had carried out trials between four-cylinder compounds and two-cylinder simples and, preferring the former, ordered its 503 class of sixty engines to the Midi design.[10]

The Nord Railway, in 1896, purchased three larger 4–4–0s from the *Société Alsacienne* which were very similar in dimensions and appearance to the Midi 1751s. They proved very successful in service and in the following year the Nord ordered twenty more, calling the whole lot the 2158 class. In reference to their size and to the striking brown livery of the Nord, they were nicknamed by the enginemen *Les Grands Chocolats*. They did excellent work on the Paris–Calais expresses and became a familiar sight to British travellers. Lord Monkswell recorded a run behind one of the *Grand Chocolats* in 1899, the year before they were superseded on the best trains by the Atlantics. The train was the *Nord*

Express, which was allowed 102 minutes for the 95 miles from Paris to St Quentin, and on this occasion it weighed 140 tons. After a slow start, due to work on the line, a distance of $11\frac{1}{4}$ miles was covered in 11 minutes 2 seconds, almost all of it up a gradient of 1 in 200. The train was then stopped by a signal, and then stopped again just beyond Creil, $31\frac{3}{4}$ miles from Paris. Starting again, 36 minutes 21 seconds after leaving Paris, the engine brought its train into St Quentin only 17 seconds late. It had covered the last $63\frac{1}{2}$ miles in 65 minutes 56 seconds, in spite of at least 2 minutes lost through having to cross to the up line for a mile or two on a stretch where the down line was being relaid. During the latter part of the run the engine hauled its train over a practically level stretch of 8.1 miles in 6 minutes 59 seconds; a speed of 69·3 m.p.h.[11] This was a fine performance, even though the load was light.

The Paris–Orleans Railway was the next to buy these engines, and their twenty-five No. 1 class 4–4–0s of 1899 were almost identical with the Midi 175Is. However, their comparative performance on this railway was not quite so impressive, because the simple expansion 2–4–2 locomotives of the Paris–Orleans were amongst the best express engines in France.[12] In fact the steam circuit of all these 4–4–0s was rather restricted, and they could be sluggish at high speeds. Du Bousquet realised this and ordered a study to be made of the steam path to find out where the trouble lay. Experiments were carried out by Barbier of the Nord on *Grand Chocolat* No. 2158 in 1897, with the result that steam circuit proportions were arrived at which included large steam chests to regulate the flow of steam between boiler and cylinders, and so lessen losses from fluctuations in the pressure caused by throttling. As a result of this investigation, du Bousquet, in 1898, enlarged the 4–4–0 design into an Atlantic with much wider steam passages. The port/cylinder area ratio was 1:8.64 in the high pressure cylinders and 1:12.21 in the low pressure; which compared with 1:10.2 high pressure and 1:14.3 low pressure in the 4–4–0. The first engine of this very famous class was shown at the Paris Exhibition of 1900—the same year, it will be remembered, that *Athara* steamed out of Swindon. The Atlantic had 13·4 inch by 25·2 inch high pressure cylinders, 22 inch by 25·2 inch low pressure cylinders, 6 foot $8\frac{1}{2}$ inch coupled wheels, 29·7 ft.^{2} grate area, 228 lb./in.^{2} boiler pressure, an adhesive weight of 37 tons, and a total weight of 70·6 tons.[13] The success of the Atlantics seems to have been largely due to du Bousquet, and it is a pity, therefore, that they are almost universally referred to in England as the 'de Glehn Atlantics'. In fact du Bousquet and de Glehn collaborated so closely that it is now impossible to say how credit for design should be divided between them. The compound system was undoubtedly de Glehn's. From the evidence of his latter work, du Bousquet probably designed the boiler and the improved steam passages. The bogie, commonly called in France *le bogie alsacien*, was designed by the *Société Alsacienne* and widely used on the P-O, Nord, Est, and Midi Railways, and, with slight differences, in Germany.[14] It is probably attributable to de Glehn and therefore justifiably called the 'de Glehn bogie' in England.

These remarkable Atlantics soon set standards of running that were unequalled anywhere else. In 1902, for instance, No. 2645, with 250 tons behind the tender, covered the 184·4 miles from Paris to Calais, start to stop, at an overall average speed of 64·4 m.p.h. gaining 27 minutes on scheduled time. Returning on the *Calais–Mediterranée* Express of 160–200 tons, some 40 minutes were gained on schedule, the engine running to Paris at an average speed of 65·6 m.p.h. including the Amiens stop, and at an average running speed of 67·5 m.p.h. In the same year No. 2656, with 161 tons, gained 25 minutes between Boulogne Ville and Paris; the 50·1 miles from Creil to Paris being covered in 40 minutes at an average speed of 75 m.p.h. Also in 1902 No. 2660 ran the 68 miles from Soissons to Paris with 200 tons in 58 minutes—an average speed of 70 m.p.h.[15] In assessing the merit of these runs it is important to remember that drivers on French railways were not allowed to exceed a speed of $75\frac{1}{2}$ m.p.h.

Performances like these startled the railway world, and several railways promptly ordered Atlantic locomotives of similar design. In 1901 the Midi acquired Atlantics identical with those of the Nord, and they were soon performing brilliantly on that railway's crack expresses: the *Sud Express*, the *Barcelona Express*, and the *Luchon Express*. In 1901, also, the P-O ordered some; but these were rather larger than those of the Nord, with 14·2 inch by 25·2 inch high pressure cylinders, 23·6 inch by 25·2 inch low pressure cylinders, 33·4 ft.[2] grate area, 35·6 tons adhesive weight, and 72·9 tons total weight. These were in service from 1903 and, with similar 4–6–0 engines, were the most powerful locomotives in France. In 1905 the Etat bought ten Atlantics which were practically the same as those of the P-O for use on the difficult line from Paris to Bordeaux via Chartres, Saumur, Niort, and Saintes.[16] But not only French engineers had taken note of these engines. In England the new Locomotive, Carriage, and Wagon Superintendent of the Great Western Railway was taking a very great interest indeed. He had his own ideas on locomotive design: how did they compare with du Bousquet's?

NOTES

1   F. Gaiser, *Die Crampton-Locomotive* (Neustadt, A. D. Haardt, 1909), p. 2.
2   A. Chapelon, 'Le Centenaire de la Locomotive Crampton et un Siècle de Progrès en Traction à Vapeur', *Mémoires de la Société des Ingenieurs Civils de France* (Mars–Avril, 1949).
3   Ibid.
4   Gaiser, op. cit., pp. 70*f*.
5   Chapelon, op. cit.
6   Ibid.
7   Ibid.
8   J. T. van Riemsdijk, 'The Compound Locomotive Part I' *Transactions of the Newcomen Society* (1970).
9   Colonel H. C. B. Rogers, *Chapelon: Genius of French Steam* (London, Ian Allan, 1972), p. 8.
10 Ibid., pp. 8–9; L. M. Vilain, *Evolution du Matériel Moteur et Roulant de la Compagnie dela Chemins de Fer du Midi* (1965), pp. 34, 65–72.
11 Lord Monkswell, *French Railways* (London, Smith, Elder & Co., 1911), pp. 96–7.
12 Rogers, op. cit., p. 9.
13 Ibid., p. 157; Van Riemsdijk, op. cit.
14 E. Sauvage and A. Chapelon, *La Machine Locomotive* (Paris & Liège, Libraraire Polytechnique Ch. Beranger, 10th edn, 1947), p. 444.
15 A. Chapelon, *La Locomotive à Vapeur* (Paris, J. B. Bailliere et Fils, 2nd edn, 1952), p. 231.
16 Rogers, op. cit., p 11; L. M. Vilain, *Una Siecle de Matériel et Traction sur le Réseau d'Orléans* (1962), pp. 37, 111–13.

Chapter 8

Churchward Takes Over

In May 1902 George Jackson Churchward succeeded William Dean as Superintendent of the Locomotive and Carriage Department. Changes became necessary as a result of his own promotion and he appointed H. C. King as Locomotive Works Manager with C. B. Collett, from the drawing office, as his Assistant. New appointments were G. H. Pearson and J. W. Cross as junior assistants to Collett with the task of carrying out experimental and development work. Though nominally subordinate to Collett, they were instructed to report directly to Churchward. (H. A. V. Bulleid tells an amusing story about this. Pearson and Cross arrived one day at Churchward's office to report and were turned away by the Chief Clerk, who had been accustomed to protect Dean from interruptions in this way. Churchward's reaction when he was acquainted with this episode was typical. He entered his office through that of the Chief Clerk and, pointing to the door of the former, said that it was his and that he would tell his people if he did not want to see them.)[1]

Churchward was greatly interested at this time in boiler circulation, and Pearson and Cross were instructed to investigate it. Some trouble had been experienced with the boiler of 4–6–0 No. 100; there had been broken stays and cracks at the junction of the boiler barrel and the firebox. Pearson and Cross discovered that the boiler circulation was indifferent and, as a result of their report, Churchward increased the size of the water legs of the firebox by curving the side plates, and the diameter of the boiler barrel at the firebox end by coning the upper part of the rear barrel plate (though leaving the lower part horizontal). The resulting sweep of the firebox ensured the success of the Churchward standard boiler. Churchward achieved, as he had set out to do, a free flow to and from the firebox and free circulation, both for the rising steam and for the incoming feed water which took its place.[2] In September 1902 one of the *Atbara* class 4–4–0 engines, *Mauritius*, which had been built just a year earlier, was given a larger boiler constructed to this

97

new design. This was to become the Standard No. 4 boiler, and *Mauritius* was the prototype of the famous *City* class, ten of which were built between March and May 1903. Except for the boiler, they were similar to the *Atbaras*, and subsequently nine more of these latter engines were provided with the No. 4 boiler, converting them to *Cities* and making a total of twenty in the class. All the 2–6–0 *Aberdares* built from the end of 1902 onwards also had the Standard No. 4 boiler, in order to give them greater power and adhesive weight on those lines which could take the heavier engine.[3]

Churchward wasted little time after he assumed office before obtaining sanction to order from the *Société Alsacienne* a compound Atlantic similar to those running on the Nord. At the meeting of the Association of Railway Locomotive Engineers on 28 November 1902, Ivatt of the Great Northern mentioned the excellent work of these locomotives, and Churchward took the opportunity to announce that he had ordered one to compare it with Great Western engines. Churchward was not, however, thinking of building compounds himself—provided that he could get comparable power output and economy of working from a simple expansion engine. However, to do this entailed, amongst other things, obtaining as much expansion of the steam in one cylinder as the compound got in two. If this could be achieved, there would still be penalties, of which such a great engineer as Churchward was doubtless well aware. Condensation in cylinders, caused by the cooling effects of the cylinder walls, is due to the difference in temperature between admission and exhaust, so that a compound engine which spreads this drop of temperature over two cylinders suffers less loss from this cause than a simple engine.[4] In fact, André Chapelon estimates the loss in the simple to be two and a half times greater than in the compound.[5] But, on the other hand, the du Bousquet-de Glehn Atlantics were complex machines to drive and maintain. French drivers were specially trained engineers, belonging to a skilled grade that firemen on French railways did not aspire to reach. British drivers could not have undertaken the duties of fitters that were expected of drivers in France, and the cost of running these Atlantics in England would therefore probably be higher than a comparable simple expansion engine.

On 19 October 1903 thirteen large packing cases containing the parts of the French Atlantic that was to become Great Western No. 102 *La France* were landed at Poplar Docks. They were sent to Swindon, where the engine was erected and connected to a standard Great Western tender. After trials, it entered service on 2 February 1904. The running of the compound Atlantic was reported in *The Railway Magazine* by Charles Rous-Marten in his monthly article *British Locomotive Practice and Performance*. He travelled behind it on its inaugural run from Paddington to Swindon, but said that neither the speed nor the load were worthy of the engine, 'which, using a mere wisp of steam, easily got to Reading 8 minutes under time, and to Swindon still earlier.' Later he made a special journey to Exeter and back, during which he recorded some striking results. The 193¾ miles from Paddington to Exeter via Bristol took 3 hours 23 minutes, which was 6¾ minutes under schedule; and this in spite of two dead stands at signals, totalling 3 minutes 45 seconds and ten slacks adding up to 20¾ minutes, so that the net time for the run was 3 hours 2½ minutes. There was no extra high speed down falling gradients, but, says Rous-Marten, 'the maximum rate attained during the whole run was on the dead-level and after several miles of absolutely flat road, when *La France* by sheer force of steam, without the slightest aid from gravitation, reached 84·9 m.p.h., the fastest I have ever noted on the dead-level unaided by gravitation.'

Before describing the engine that Churchward designed to equal du Bousquet-de Glehn performance, it is necessary to jump a year ahead, to 18 March 1904, when a paper was read by the eminent French locomotive engineer, Edouard Sauvage, to the Institution of Mechanical Engineers, on the subject of compound locomotives. Sauvage's paper was of particular interest to British locomotive engineers because of the recent construction by the Midland Railway of compound engines using a system that Sauvage had designed. In 1887 Sauvage, then of the Nord Railway, had built in that company's Works a three-cylinder 2-6-0 compound locomotive with one inside high pressure cylinder and two outside low pressure cylinders. The outside cranks were set at ninety degrees to each other, whilst the inside crank bisected the obtuse angle between them. It was the only one of its type, though it was very successful in the task for which it was designed—the haulage of fast goods trains. But though this engine was the solitary example in France, the idea was taken up by W. M. Smith, Chief Draughtsman on the North Eastern Railway, who in 1898 converted a two-cylinder compound 4-4-0 engine to this system. Then in 1901-03 S. W. Johnson of the Midland Railway built five 4-4-0 engines at Derby as compounds on the Sauvage-Smith system. The first two had, like the engines of both Sauvage and Smith, independent reversing gears for the high pressure and low pressure cylinders, but the last three had only one set of reversing gear to operate all three sets of valve gear. At this time Deeley had just taken over from

Johnson, and his modification of these engines was destined to become famous on both the Midland and the London Midland & Scottish Railways.

In his paper Sauvage outlined the development of compound locomotives in France and said that they had enabled French railways to run faster and heavier trains without any large increased consumption of coal. He thought that it would be difficult to build a simple expansion locomotive that was quite the equal of the latest compounds, because, with the ordinary valve gear steam at such a high pressure could not be so well used as in a compound.

In the subsequent discussion Churchward said that the compound locomotive had been brought to greater perfection in France than in any other country, which was why he had purchased *La France*. He believed, however, that 'no really fair and square tests' had ever been made between the compound and simple expansion systems. Trials had been carried out between compound locomotives with a pressure of 200 lb./in.^{2}, and simples with 175 lb./in.^{2}; but he would no doubt be told that it was believed impossible with any known valve gear to use the higher pressure to advantage in a simple cylinder. He thought this had yet to be proved, and he had fitted a simple engine with 18 inch by 30 inch cylinders and a boiler pressure of 225 lb./in.^{2} with the deliberate idea of finding out whether such improvements could be made in the valve gear and consequent steam distribution as to enable steam of that pressure to be used as efficiently in a simple engine as in a compound. On trials, he had made the powers of a simple engine (with 200 lb./in.^{2} pressure) and *La France* at high speed practically equal. In the latter he had used the recommended cut-offs of 55 per cent in the high pressure and 65 per cent in the low pressure cylinders, whilst in the simple engine he had used 20 to 25 per cent. He added that it would appear to be ambitious to expect, with these respective cut-offs, that the simple should develop the same power as the compound, 'But,' he added, 'I am pleased to say that with the assistance of an efficient staff, a good deal of very hard work, and a determination to see what could be done with valve gear, I believe such improvements have been made with the steam distribution that a satisfactory result can be obtained from as high a cut-off as 15 to 20 per cent.' Both *La France* and his simple engine with 200 lb./in.^{2} pressure, i.e. 4–6–0 No. 98 had produced a drawbar pull of two tons at 70 m.p.h., and from the 225 lb./in.^{2} engine he expected to get two tons at 75 m.p.h. on a shorter cut-off.

Now, because it was his valve gear, together with his boiler design,

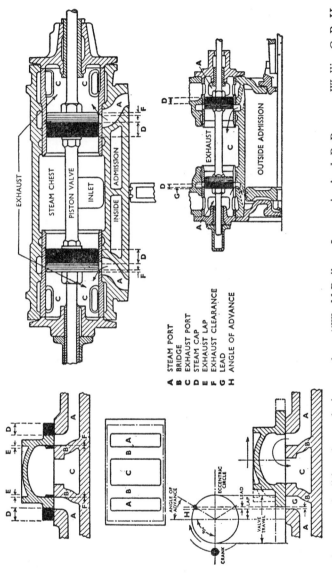

EXHAUST

STEAM CHEST

PISTON VALVE

INLET

INSIDE ADMISSION

EXHAUST

OUTSIDE ADMISSION

A STEAM PORT
B BRIDGE
C EXHAUST PORT
D STEAM CAP
E EXHAUST LAP
F EXHAUST CLEARANCE
G LEAD
H ANGLE OF ADVANCE

ANGLE OF ADVANCE

ECCENTRIC CIRCLE

LEAD
LAP

VALVE TRAVEL

CRANK

Figure 10 A slide valve and piston valves. ('*World Railway Locomotives*', ed. P. Ransome-Wallis; C. R. H. Simpson, '*The Reciprocating Steam Locomotive*')

that was responsible for the outstanding performance of Churchward's engines, it is important to consider what he had done about the former. Lap is essential to the expansive working of a steam locomotive and is obtained by increasing the length of the valve face so that the admission edges of the ports are overlapped when the valve is in mid-position. This enables the driver to cut off the admission of steam to the cylinder at a percentage of the stroke which is under his control, so that the remainder of the work in the cylinder is done by the steam already there. If throttling of the steam is to be avoided (which is necessary for a good steam circuit) the engine should be worked with the regulator fully open. For economical running maximum use must be made of the expansion of steam, and on a simple engine this entails running with a short cut-off. (This is not so necessary with a compound locomotive because expansion is carried out in two stages in successive cylinders.) With the conventional valve gear of the time, to which Sauvage referred, the port openings were gradually reduced as the motion was linked up, until the entry of steam into the cylinder and (more important) its exit to exhaust became so restricted as to cancel out the advantage of the full regulator opening. On most railways it was the practice to compromise by running their simple engines with cut-offs of from 25 to 30 per cent and with the regulator partially open and so throttling the steam. Churchward wanted 15 per cent with full regulator, and this demanded much bigger port openings when the motion was fully linked up.

The design of valves is a very complex subject which it is not intended to describe in detail here. The three most important things which the designer can alter are the length of the lap, the length that the valve travels, and the lead (which is the amount of port opened to steam just before the piston reaches the end of its stroke). What Churchward did, in short, was to increase the valve travel by over 50 per cent of that normally used, to nearly double the customary size of the laps, and to leave the lead alone. The result of this was to increase at all cut-offs the steam port opening and the expansion period, and to get a full exhaust port opening over a long period. In full gear the steam port opening was actually more than required owing to the very long travel of the valve, but this allowed the increased openings at reduced cut-offs as the valve travel shortened.[6] Put like this it may sound simple, but to design valves to obtain these results entailed, as Churchward said, very hard work. The theoretical advantages of long-travel valves were, of course, well known, but many engineers disliked the idea for fear of greatly increased wear. To a certain extent this fear was justified with slide valves, but much less so with piston valves because of the decreased friction. In addition, what many engineers forgot, was that if an engine is habitually working at a very short cut-off, the long-travel valve is actually travelling little farther than a short travel valve at a longer cut-off.

In modern steam locomotives the design practice due to Churchward's genius has been incorporated so widely that it is difficult now to appreciate the brilliance of his ideas and how they diverged from the normal standards of the time. Nevertheless, he was essentially a modest man, and it may be this which prevented him from seeing that at this period his steam circuit was so much better than du Bousquet's that the test he was conducting between compound and simple engines were not really 'fair and square'. In fact the only really fair comparative tests ever carried out were those on the SNCF between de Caso's 232R and 232S 4–6–4 locomotives of 1940, which were identical, except that the former were three-cylinder simples and the latter four-cylinder compounds. On trial the compound engines showed an economy of 12 per cent over the simples.

It is time to return to the detail of Churchward's engines. The boiler fitted to *Mauritius* having proved successful, similar modifications were made to the Standard No. 1 boiler designed for No. 100 and Churchward's next 4–6–0, No. 98 (later 2998 *Ernest Cunard*) was built in March 1903 with this modified No. 1. No. 98, however, embodied many other improvements as well as some features that Churchward had taken from American practice. Pains had been taken to secure a very free exhaust, for Churchward insisted that this was of far greater importance than admission. The 18 inch by 30 inch cylinders had inside admission piston valves of diameter no less than 10 inches, with steam ports $1\frac{3}{4}$ inches wide and exhaust ports of $4\frac{1}{4}$ inches, driven by Stephenson link motion inside the frames through rocking shafts. The valves had a long travel and long steam lap. The cylinders were cast in halves, bolted together in the centre, and incorporated in a cast saddle carrying the round smokebox. The coupled wheels were of 6 foot $8\frac{1}{2}$ inch diameter, the grate area was 27 ft.[2], and the boiler pressure was 200 lb./in.[2]. To suit the construction of the cylinders, the framing at the front followed American practice; each side consisting of a thick rectangular plate attached to the buffer beam at the front end. The back end was splayed to a reduced thickness to suit the depth of the main frame plates; the front and main frames being joined immediately behind the cylinders.[7]

Churchward's emphasis on the importance of the exhaust is endorsed by Chapelon, who writes: The correct functioning of the exhaust plays a decisive part, and experience shows that when an effective draught under all conditions has been achieved, even a boiler with a small grate will allow much greater powers to be developed than where the boiler has very large dimensions but the exhaust is defective.' And: 'In the design of an express engine the exhaust side is much more important than the admission side. It is to the former that attention must be paid from the very first; providing for the ports as large an area as is needed and adopting the most perfect possible type of exhaust.[8]

Chapelon stresses the importance of increasing the cross section of the steam passages from the regulator to the exhaust, and in this respect Churchward had achieved more than any contemporary locomotive engineer either in Great Britain or abroad. The large piston valves, 10 inches in diameter, allowed a considerable steam chest volume, and a ratio of port area to cylinder cross section of probably 1:7. In addition, the long stroke of the cylinders with straight ports at the extremities resulted in the valve heads being widely separated, with a consequent still greater increase in the steam chest volume.[9] No. 98 was, without doubt, the most outstanding engine in Great Britain at the time of its construction. E. C. Poultney calls it[10] 'the keystone of the arch'; and indeed it was, because every subsequent outstanding British engine owed its success in some degree to the incorporation of principles and some aspects of design which appeared first in No. 98.

Two other prototype locomotives appeared at about the same time as No. 98; No. 97, a 2–8–0 heavy freight engine (the first of its type in the country) and No. 99, a 2–6–2 side tank for mixed traffic working. No. 97 (later No. 2800) had the standard 4 foot $7\frac{1}{2}$ inch coupled wheels of a locomotive intended for mineral train working. As compared with the 4–6–0, these small wheels entailed a downward set to the front rectangular plate, or more properly bar, frame. With the 6 foot $8\frac{1}{2}$ inch wheels of the 4–6–0, the bar frame could pass below the cylinders at buffer beam height; it was therefore straight and buffer beam shocks could only compress it. But with the downward set of the 2–8–0's frame, such shocks would tend to bend as well as to compress. To counter this, and the possible collapse of the front end in a serious collision, the stay plate in line with the slide bar brackets was extended upwards, close to but not touching the boiler barrel, and ready to support it in the event of damage to the front end. Later, two round bar stays were added, connecting the buffer beam to the underside of the smokebox to assist in taking buffer shocks. The tank engine, No. 99, with 5 foot 6 inch wheels, had less set to the bar frame but was given the same precautions as

No. 97. No. 97 had the same Standard No. 1 boiler as No. 98, but No. 99 was given the Standard No. 2 boiler. Both these engines had the successful pony truck fitted to the *Aberdares*, and No. 99 had the radial axlebox at the trailing end used on the 2–4–2 tank.[11]

While these new locomotives were steaming out from Swindon, Churchward aired some of his thinking during the discussion of a paper on *American Locomotive Practice* read before the Institution of Civil Engineers on 31 March 1903. (This was, of course, a year before Sauvage's paper mentioned above.) He pointed out that a sloping top to the firebox was practically a necessity with long boilers, because when the brake was applied the water ran to the front end to such an extent that the back of the roof sheet was uncovered, and by dropping the back of the box by three inches the benefit of three inches of water was obtained on application of the brake. He drew attention to the problems presented in the design of piston valves, which had given considerable trouble and were undoubtedly one of the most troublesome pieces of mechanism. He had set before him the task of curing the defects if possible, because he felt quite sure that engineers would never have the chance of utilising the utmost power of the locomotive and bringing it, in economy, within anything like the reach of the compound (obviously thinking of the French Atlantics) without the use of piston valves. Because of the success over many years of plain snap rings on pistons of 18 to 20 inches in diameter running at high speeds, he did not think there was any reason to despair of getting a tight piston valve before long. Piston valves were supposed to use more steam than flat valves, and this belief was held not only widely but strongly on the Great Western. But one piston valve engine weighing 68 tons 10 hundredweight, i.e. 4–6–0 No. 100, on its first 4000 miles, working the heaviest expresses between Bristol and Exeter, had consumed only 33·5 pounds of coal per mile. While piston valves remained tight their economy was, if anything, superior to that of the ordinary flat valve. Designing outside cylinders with piston valves on the Great Western had entailed coming down nearly to a bar frame at the front end to get a reasonable arrangement of the piston valve. No trouble had so far been experienced with it, and, although it might be a little more expensive to build, it made a better arrangement of valves and ports than was possible with a slab frame.

Churchward's standard boilers were expensive, and it was therefore of some importance that they were given good water; for unsatisfactory water is the prime cause of boiler deterioration. The Nitrate Railways in Chile in the 1930s provide an extreme case. On this line the water was so bad that after plants had been installed at various points for treating water by a special process, fuel consumption dropped by 30 per cent and the number of locomotives required to cover the service was reduced by 25 per cent.[12] Gooch's comments on the bad supply of water at Swindon have been mentioned; and for many years water was provided for Swindon Works and running shed by the local canal company's Coate reservoir for £300 a year. In 1863 one of Gooch's pupils, who knew the local countryside well, told him that the best spring near Swindon was at Latton, just north of Cricklade. The suggestion, however, was not acted on.

As the town of Swindon expanded, a company was formed to supply some of the additional water needed from a spring at Wroughton, south of the town. But most of the water for the Works and running shed was obtained by running water trains of old tenders from Kemble, where there was good water, to Swindon.

In 1898 Churchward's notice was drawn to the suggestion of 1863, for the water situation at the Works was becoming serious because of the needs of the rapidly growing town. Latton, however, was near to the line of the Midland & South Western Junction Railway, and Churchward preferred to install a 15 inch water main running alongside the Gloucester branch over the $12\frac{1}{2}$ miles from Kemble to Swindon, and this was completed in December 1903. The pipe line being mainly down hill, the water had sufficient head to fill the high level storage tanks in Swindon Works by gravity alone.[13]

When *La France* arrived, another 4–6–0 was being built for competitive running with the French engine. This was No. 171 *Albion* (later No. 2971) which was completed in December 1903, and was the engine with 225 lb./in.^{2} pressure referred to by Churchward in the discussion on the Sauvage paper. Apart from the higher pressure, *Albion* was similar to No. 98. The increase of 25 pounds was intended to make the pressure practically the same as that of the French engine which was 228 lb./in.^{2} a boiler of much the same size. Comparative trials between the two engines were carried out for some months. However, *Albion*, being a 4–6–0, had about 50 per cent more adhesive weight than *La France*; so, to make the comparison still closer, Churchward altered *Albion* into an Atlantic by replacing the trailing pair of coupled wheels by a two-wheel truck. These trials are discussed in the next chapter.

Two more prototypes appeared in 1904. One was No. 115, a 2–6–2 side tank engine which was a smaller version of No. 99 and was intended primarily for working on branch lines where route restrictions prohibited the use of heavier locomotives. It had a new coned Standard No. 5 boiler with a working pressure of 165 lb./in.², 16½ inch by 24 inch cylinders, and 4 foot 1½ inch coupled wheels. The other prototype was the outside cylinder 4–4–0 envisaged in 1901 for the Shrewsbury–Hereford line; though Webb, whose objections to the use of 4–6–0s on that line had been responsible for the design, had retired the previous year. It had the Standard No. 4 boiler and 6 foot 8½ inch coupled wheels, and was really a shortened version of No. 98.

When Churchward became Locomotive Superintendent, the Great Western Railway was meeting increased competition in suburban areas from electric street tramways and horse-drawn buses. To counter this competition the Great Western Board decided to introduce rail motor cars so that more frequent services could be provided on both suburban and country branch lines. Trials took place early in 1903 with one of Dugald Drummond's rail motors which he had designed for the joint LSWR/LBSCR East Southsea service. As a result of these trials the first Great Western rail motor cars came into service on 12 October 1903. They were the first carriages designed by Churchward, and American influence was apparent in their slab-sided bodies and large windows. Another innovation was an open saloon type interior, with seats on either side of a central aisle. They only catered for one class and some of them had a section partitioned off for non-smokers. At one end of the car was the driving bogie, whilst the other end was carried on a 8 foot bolster bogie which, for the first time, replaced the Dean suspension bogie. The boiler was vertical, with a pressure of 160 lb./in.², and was mounted on the underframe above the driving bogie. This latter was a modified form of the suspension system, in which the round base of the boiler was used in place of a centre pin, acting through pads on the underframe members. The outside cylinders were 12 inches by 16 inches and drove on to a pair of 3 foot 6 inch diameter wheels with inside bearings. Balanced slide valves were operated by Walschaerts gear.[14]

In the earlier cars there was a vestibule at the trailing end by which the passengers entered and left. There was also a position for the driver in this vestibule, for use when the car was running with the engine in the rear, at which were fitted a handle connected by rodding to the regulator, a vacuum brake application valve, a cord connected to the whistle, and a bell communication with the fireman. Vacuum was maintained by means of a small ejector.[15]

The first two cars operated on the busy Stroud Valley line between Chalford and Stonehouse, and they had folding steps at the vestibule end so that passengers could mount or alight at level crossings. However, the level crossing stop was replaced before long by short platforms called 'halts' which had easy access from a public road. At one time there were nearly a hundred cars distributed over the Great Western, and a large number of spare motor bogies were held so that the overhaul of power units did not entail taking cars off the road. The services were very popular and their institution led to the construction or expansion of housing estates close to the halts. So many extra passengers were attracted that, during the busy periods of the day, trailer cars were attached with seating similar to that of the motor cars and with a driving compartment fitted with duplicate controls at the outer end. The very popularity of the cars led eventually to their replacement, because the engine was too small to tackle the extra weight of the trailer car on many of the routes. Auto-trains were therefore introduced from 1905 to replace the motor cars where the traffic had got beyond their capacity. An ordinary tank engine, such as a Wolverhampton 517 class 0-4-2, was fitted with controls which could be extended as required. It had sufficient power to work four coaches, two in front and two behind. The advantages of this arrangement was that the engine could be detached and sent to a depot for servicing, and it could also run at a higher speed than the 30 m.p.h. maximum of the motor cars.[16]

In 1904 Churchward brought out his revolutionary *Dreadnought* coaching stock, nearly 70 feet long, 9 feet 6 inches wide, mounted on 9 foot plate frame bolster bogies, and without the Dean clerestory roof. These big carriages had been provided at the specific request of the traffic department because of the increase in the number of passengers, who had been attracted by the improved services. The length of this stock led to the replacement of the Dean suspension bogie, because there was a limit to the angularity to which the suspension bolts could go on sharp curves, and this had been more than reached. A conventional bolster bogie with equaliser bars over the axleboxes, in conjunction with helical springs, had consequently to be developed.[17] The nickname *Dreadnought* was acquired some little time after their introduction, for it was derived from the battleship of that name which was launched in February 1906. Restaurant cars of this pattern were built first and they rather spoiled the symmetry of trains by being marshalled with Dean clerestory compartment carriages. The ordinary *Dreadnought* compartment carriages began to appear in the middle of 1905, and 3 seven-coach sets were built for the new *Cornish Riviera Express*. They had first- and third-class accommodation only, because it had been decided to withdraw second-class seating from limited expresses running between Paddington and Penzance. The third-class passengers, however, had less, rather than greater, comfort because their compartments were very cramped with only 5 feet 6 inches between partitions. Compartment doors were dispensed with and passengers entered and left by end and central vestibules, the corridor changing sides at the latter. Churchward disliked doors to each compartment because they broke up the side framing of the body and made the coaches weaker than those used in America, with end doors and long frame members. As with his locomotives, Churchward was before his time with his carriages; but not so successfully, because the passengers did not like the new layout, and doors to compartments were restored on later construction. Though electric lighting had been introduced on the New Milford boat train sets, the *Dreadnoughts* were lit by gas with the incandescent mantle, which was first used on the Great Western in 1905. Two years later it was superseded by the inverted burner.[18]

In 1903 a number of carriages were painted dark brown with a gold lining. It was the start of a series of experiments, which resulted in the introduction in 1908 of an overall chocolate lake livery, lined out in yellow; and it was not till after Churchward's retirement that the traditional chocolate and cream was restored.

NOTES

1 H. A. V. Bulleid, *Master Builders of Steam* (London, Ian Allan, 1963), p. 107.
2 K. J. Cook, 'The Late G. J. Churchward's Locomotive Development on the Great Western Railway', *Journal of the Institution of Locomotive Engineers* Paper No. 492 (March–April 1950).
3 A. Chapelon, letter to the author.
   Sir William Stanier, 'George Jackson Churchward, Chief Mechanical Engineer, Great Western Railway', *Transactions of the Newcomen Society*, (1960); H. M. Le Fleming, *Dean's Larger Tender Engines, The Locomotives of the Great Western Railway*, Part 7 (RCTS, 1954), pp. G33*f*.
4 A. Chapelon, 'La Locomotive Compound, son Etat Actuel, son Avenir', *Science et Industrie* (1933–34).
5 Ibid.
6 C. S. Lake and A. Reidinger, *Locomotive Valves and Valve Gear* (London, Percival Marshal & Co., revd edn, 1951), pp. 48, 91–2.
7 Cook, op. cit.
   H. Holcroft, *An Outline of Great Western Locomotive Practice* (London, Locomotive Publishing Co., 1957), pp. 83–4.
8 A. Chapelon, *La Locomotive à Vapeur* (Paris, J. B. Baillière et Fils, 2nd end, 1952), pp. 139–140.

9   E. C. Poultney, *British Express Locomotive Development* (London, George Allen & Unwin, 1952), pp. 66–7.

10   Ibid., p. 66.

11   Holcroft, op. cit., pp. 84–5.

12   A. Morton Bell, *Locomotives; their Construction, Maintenance, and Operation* (London, Virtue & Co., 3rd edn, 1936), vol. I, pp. 202*f*.

13   H. Holcroft, letter to the author.

14   Ibid.; M. Harris, *Great Western Coaches: 1890–1954* (Newton Abbot, David & Charles, 1966), pp. 61*f*.

15   H. Holcroft, letter to the author.

16   Ibid.

17   Ibid.

18   Harris, op. cit., p. 39.

Chapter 9

Policy Decided

'The French compound will pull two tons at seventy miles an hour on the drawbar, and it takes a remarkably good locomotive to do that.' So said Churchward in the discussion on his paper *Large Locomotive Boilers*, read to the Institution of Mechanical Engineers in February 1906. Nevertheless, good though *La France* was, Churchward's own *Albion* had performed so well in the comparative trials that there was little to choose between the two engines in power and economy.

In the meantime the Paris–Orleans Railway had been carrying out tests with the first of their Atlantics (larger than those of the Nord) in the second half of 1903. The purpose of the trials was to investigate the power developed by the engine and its fuel consumption. Paul Conté, an Engineer-in-Chief on the P–O, described the trials and their results in an article published in the *Revue Générale des Chemins de Fer* of July 1904. The maximum indicated horsepower recorded was 1890, and this was whilst the engine was hauling a train of 352 tons at a speed varying from 70 to 72 m.p.h. up a gradient of 1 in 500 and with cut-offs of 53 per cent high pressure and 65 per cent low pressure. The gross, or uncorrected, drawbar horsepower averaged 980 during this effort. On 2 December 1903, with the same train of 352 tons, the engine ran from Paris to Tours at an average speed, excluding stops, of a fraction under 60 m.p.h. On 27 November 1903 an average indicated horsepower of 1300 was recorded, the rate of combustion being 107 pounds of coal per square foot of grate area per hour.[1]

Churchward must have read the account of these trials, and the results were no doubt sufficiently impressive for him to want to see how these larger compounds compared with his simple expansion engines. He accordingly obtained authority to order two P–O type Atlantics from the *Société Alsacienne*. There was an advantage in having two of them because if he only had one its performance might be below the normal standard. (This was a not uncommon occurrence with steam locomotives, and he may have had an uneasy feeling that *La France* was not behaving quite as well as her sisters on the home ground.) The two new engines, which became No. 103 *President* and No. 104 *Alliance* (in reference to the new *Entente Cordiale* between Great Britain and France), were delivered to the Great Western in June 1905.

Churchward was not only trying simples against compounds, but also 4–6–0s against 4–4–2s. Of his own express engines, he built during 1905 thirteen more Atlantics similar to *Albion* and six more 4–6–0s which were identical with the Atlantics except for the wheel arrangement and the ashpans. The Atlantics were given names from Sir Walter Scott's 'Waverley' novels, many of which had been borne by Gooch's *Waverley* class 4–4–0 locomotives, while some of the 4–6–0s were named after Great Western directors. All the Atlantics were so built that they could be converted later to 4–6–0s if desired. There was an unexpected problem when the engines first went into service; for W. A. (later Sir William) Stanier, Assistant Divisional Locomotive Superintendent at Paddington, had to report to Churchward that the Atlantics would not steam. Churchward sent for him and asked what the hell was the matter with them. The ashpans of the Atlantics were straight bottomed instead of being shaped round the rear coupled axle as on the 4–6–0s, but *Albion*'s ashpan had been left unaltered when she had been converted from a 4–6–0 to a 4–4–2. Stanier said that the shape of the ashpan was the only difference he could see. Churchward exclaimed immediately that he thought Stanier had got it and they were restricting the airflow. This was indeed the trouble, for one of the Atlantics was provided with a 4–6–0 type ashpan and the steaming was as free as in *Albion*. The remaining Atlantics then had their ashpans similarly changed; which had the added advantage that they were the more ready for conversion to 4–6–0s, should this step be decided.[2] (In fact, they were so converted in 1912–13.) In order to make the numbers of the four-coupled and six-coupled engines more even, ten more 4–6–0s were ordered in 1906 and were given names beginning with *Lady*.[3]

Further trials between Churchward's engines and all three French compounds confirmed his opinion that in power and economy there was little to choose between simples and compounds, and that therefore, having regard to the extra cost and complexity of the compounds, he would not be justified in building them. On the other hand, the compounds, with their four cylinders, divided drive, and balanced reciprocating masses, were much smoother riding than the Great Western engines with their two outside cylinders. Churchward decided that it

26 French compound Atlantic No. 104 *Alliance*, fitted with a Swindon
Standard No. 1 boiler. (*British Railways*)

27 Two-cylinder Atlantic No. 171 *Albion*, built for comparative trials with
La France. (*British Railways*)

28 Four-cylinder Atlantic No. 40 (later *North Star*), built as a result of
experience with the French Atlantics. (Note the fully coned barrel.) (*British
Railways*)

29 One of the first batch of two-cylinder 4–6–0s, No. 175 *Viscount Churchill*,
for comparison with the Great Western Atlantics. (*British Railways*)

30 Four-cylinder *Star* class 4–6–0 No. 4016 *Knight of the Garter*. The engine has Holcroft's curves to the footplating at front and rear. (*British Railways*)

31 Du Bosquet's development of the French Atlantic for greater adhesion; Nord 3513 class 4–6–0 No. 3.514. (*Chapelon collection*)

32 Nord 3513 class 4–6–0 No. 3.538, with superheated boiler, showing the outside steam pipes in a similar position to those of *Alliance* with a Swindon boiler. (*Chapelon collection*)

33 The ultimate development of 3513 class (later 230D) 4–6–0, with Lemaitre exhaust; somewhat equivalent to the *Castle* development from *Stars*. (*Chapelon collection*)

34 Two-cylinder 4–6–0 *Robins Bolitho* at Swindon on a Paddington to Fishguard express on 25 September 1906. The leading carriage is a Dean clerestory, followed by a *Concertina*, then another clerestory, followed by another *Concertina*, with a third clerestory bringing up the rear. All are still in the chocolate and cream livery. (*British Railways*)

would be worth building a similar type of four-cylinder engine, but as a simple instead of a compound, and with two sets of valve gear instead of the four, which the French engines had on account of the independent reversing gear to the high pressure and low pressure cylinders. Churchward admired the beautiful workmanship of the compounds and their light Walschaerts valve gear, which he described as a 'watchmaker's job'. But it was too light to drive two valves and he would need something heavier. He liked the French inside big ends and decided to adopt them. He liked the bogie too, and two years later he adopted that as well.

Charles Rous-Marten admired the French compounds, and he wrote of them as follows in the last article on *British Locomotive Practice and Performance* for *The Railway Magazine* before his premature death on 20 April 1908:[4]

'Mr Churchward designed and built some new engines of the "Atlantic" or 4–4–2 type, with approximately the same boiler power and steam pressure as the Frenchmen—I do not take into account the six-coupled bogies in this connection, as their vast superiority in adhesion-weight made a just comparison with four-coupled engines impossible, especially on such a road as the South Devon. The result of that comparison has been told by Inspector R. H. Smith as being that the British single-expansion engine could haul 50 tons more than the French compounds, and, I understand, at no larger cost in coal consumption. Here I should remark, in passing, that I fully realise how many unexpressed factors may exist that would materially affect the comparison; such, for instance, as difference of fuel and working. For the moment I take the fact officially reported—that when competing on equal terms of boiler-power, steam-pressure, and road, the British engines, *when they were on equal terms as regarded those points,* beat the French compounds. The latter, as abroad, did most excellent work, but the former did "more excellenter".

'This, then, brings us to one definite point at least—that, according to the Great Western Railway's trials, given approximate equality of condition, including boiler-power and steam-pressure, you get approximate equality of result with a slight advantage on the side of the single-expansion Britishers. Assuming that this result is not vitiated by any of the various disturbing factors at which I have hinted, then the obvious inference would be that it becomes hardly worth while to go to the extra expense of building compounds when non-compounds can be produced which will do quite as well, or slightly better. But I am not yet prepared to accept that conclusion. For, apart from the as-yet-unsettled doubt as to disturbing factors, I feel bound to point out that, in certain classes of work, I have not yet found the French compounds equalled in this country. Even on the Great Western itself I have never yet known any other engines ascend the Hemerdon and Burlescombe banks with light loads so smartly as the French compounds, nor have I known any British locomotive, even when hard pressed, to attain what I have long taken as the standard of the French compounds, viz., to *maintain* a rate of 60 miles an hour with 300 tons behind the tender up a long continuous gradient of 1 in 200. . . .'

Rous-Marten continues with other examples of French compound performance which he has not seen equalled by British locomotives. Then he says:

'I should like to see special tests made of British engines with the view of like results. Do not misunderstand me. I do not say the British engines could *not* do it; I see no reason why certain British engines should not be able to do it, and I think it very likely that they *could*. All I say is that I have never seen it done, and that until I *have* seen it done I cannot admit that the last word has been said on the vexed question of compound *versus* non-compound.

'But there is yet another phase of the big problem. Even assuming that all these trials were made, that all resulted in favour of the compounds, and that the results obtained on the Great Western Railway proved to be rendered inconclusive through the ascertained influence of disturbing factors, even so the question would remain: Are or are not the assumed advantages of compounding purchased at too high a price? Here we are at present without any definite authentic information.'

The comments by this extremely shrewd observer of the railway scene are extremely interesting, and he ends with the question that British locomotive engineers were to be asking up to the end of the days of steam. By implication, Rous-Marten feels that even if Churchward's tests were not a true comparison between simple and compound, he was still justified in preferring to build the former.

Because he had not yet made up his mind as between the relative advantages of 4–6–0s and Atlantics, Churchward came to the conclusion that it would be better to build his four-cylinder engine as an Atlantic, thus enabling him to make the most exact comparison yet between simple and compound. Authority for its construction was given on 19 July 1905.

This historic locomotive was given the number 40 (which was later to be altered to 4000). It was completed in April 1906 and in the following September it was given the name *North Star*, after its famous predecessor which had been broken up a few months before. Interest in preserving notable steam locomotives was unfortunately not as strong in 1905 as it is today, and Churchward had tried unsuccessfully to find some institution willing to accept the old *North Star* and the equally famous 8 foot 'single' *Lord of the Isles*. He had no strong sentimental regard himself for these relics of a past which he had been only to anxious to see discarded, and he needed the room that they occupied in the Works. And so the following letter was sent to the Great Western Board:

'Great Western Railway
   Locomotive & Carriage Department
     Engineers Office
      Swindon   16 December 1905
'OLD B.G. ENGINES "NORTH STAR" AND "LORD OF THE ISLES"
   'These engines are occupying valuable space in our Shops at Swindon. They have been offered to several Institutions without success, and I beg to recommend that authority be given for them to be destroyed.'
   (*Signed*) 'G. J. Churchward'[5]

If R. F. Hanks had been Chairman at Paddington at the time (as he was to be many years later) the authority would not have been given. But unfortunately there was apparently no one on the Board with his strong feeling for the Great Western past, and the two engines were broken up.

No. 40 had a Standard No. 1 boiler, but the taper extended over its whole length instead of being confined to the rear barrel plate. The cylinder arrangement was similar to that of the French compounds, except that the inside cylinders were farther forward to enable the connecting rods to be of practically the same length; for it was intended that the four valves should be operated by two sets of valve gear and rocking levers. The disposition of the cylinders prohibited the use of the American-type bar frame construction, which had been adopted for the two-cylinder engines, and No. 40 had plate frames throughout.

Inside Stephenson's valve gear had been fitted to the two-cylinder engines, but this arrangement was not practicable with a four-cylinder locomotive because Churchward's large axleboxes and crankpins left insufficient room. Churchward did not like outside valve gear. One reason was that there was not, in his opinion, space within the loading for a gear with links of the requisite size; a further reason was that Churchward's solid bush ends to the connecting rods would entail partly dismantling an outside gear to allow of a connecting rod being removed. But one suspects that a third reason was predominant: that Churchward just did not like outside fittings because he thought they spoilt the appearance of his engines. The valve gear would therefore have to be inside, and as Stephenson's type would not fit it would have to be Walschaerts. However, this decision says R. F. Hanks, who worked on them as an apprentice, made the four-cylinder engines difficult to maintain and repair.[6]

Churchward, contrary to frequently expressed opinion, was very sensitive about the appearance of his engines. During the previously mentioned discussion on his paper, *Large Locomotive Boilers*, in 1906, James Stirling, late Locomotive Superintendent of the South Eastern Railway, said of Churchward's engines, 'They are novel in shape and expensive in construction: they may be good but they are certainly not "bonnie", to use a Scotch expression.' Churchward in reply said, 'I know that I have been accused of spoiling the appearance of the British locomotive as much as any man in the country, but I take exception to that statement. In my opinion, there is no canon of art in regard to the appearance of a locomotive or a machine, except that which an engineer has set up for himself, by observing from time to time types of engines which he has been led from his nursery days upwards to admire.' And so we take a look at the pictures of the South Devon 4-4-0 tank engines of G. J. Churchward's childhood and youth—the engines which he admired when at school in Totnes and on which he worked as a pupil at Newton Abbot—with their fully exposed driving wheels and austere functional lines, and we see that No. 98 was far closer to them in appearance than to the graceful locomotives of William Dean. Yet Churchward, peculiarly sensitive to criticism, decided that his engines could be made still better looking, and H. Holcroft, recently transferred from Wolverhampton, was given the task. Holcroft had preconceived notions on how this could be done, and he says that he took the 4-6-0 and proceeded to deal with it accordingly. He connected the drop in level between platforms at the front end by means of a simple curve, and repeated it in reverse at the front plate of the cab to bring the side of the cab down to the level of the tender frame. This treatment, he says, was much liked, and he had the 'satisfaction of having "shaped the ends" of Great Western locomotives as long as their construction continued'.[7]

That Churchward was proud of the appearance of his engines is confirmed by the following story told to the author by W. N. Pellow: 'I remember when W. A. Stanier was sent to the USA to study some of the ways of American engineers, and came back with scores of ideas and suggestions. A number of these the old man rejected out of hand. He did not wish, he said, to spoil the clean lines of his locomotives.[8]

E. C. Poultney saw No. 40 nearing completion in the erecting shops in 1906 through, he says, Churchward's courtesy.[9] The boiler pressure was 225 lb./in^2. The outside cylinders drove the trailing coupled axle, and the inside cylinders the leading axle, the connecting rods being respectively 8 feet and 7 feet 10 inches long. The four cylinders were $14\frac{1}{8}$ inches by 26 inches, and each had 8 inch diameter piston valves with port dimensions on the bushings of 25 inches by $1\frac{1}{4}$ inches steam and 25 inches by 3 inches exhaust. This gives a port area to cylinder cross-section ratio of probably 1:8. The valve gear was a modified form of Walschaerts in which the expansion links were actuated by links from the crossheads, so that the crosshead on one side actuated the expansion link on the other, thus avoiding the need for eccentrics.[10] This valve gear was devised by a draughtsman, W. H. Pearce, who had designed the Stephenson gear fitted to the two-cylinder engines. On account of the expansion link levers, it was called the 'scissors' gear. But although Pearce did not know it, other engineers had conceived the same idea. The first seems to have been the Belgian engineer Stévart. R. M. Deeley, when Works Manager at Derby, designed a similar gear, but he too did not know that he had been preceded by Stévart. He showed it to S. W. Johnson, the Locomotive Superintendent. Johnson was not impressed, but when Deeley succeeded him in 1904 he decided to use his scissors gear and applied for a patent, which was granted in 1906. It was duly fitted to the Midland 990 class 4–4–0 simple expansion locomotives, of which the first appeared in 1907. However, this novel aspect of the 990s caused little stir in locomotive engineering circles because Churchward's No. 40, with a similar valve gear, had appeared the previous year. An incensed Deeley wrote a strong letter of protest to Churchward, and it has been said that as a result of this no more Great Western engines were built with the scissors gear. But there is a Derby story that Churchward told Deeley to go to hell, and this seems more in keeping with his character. In view of the close attention that Churchward paid to locomotive events elsewhere, it is probable that he knew about Stévart's gear and that therefore Deeley's patent could not prevent him using this system if he wished to. In fact he was probably put off it for a very different reason.

If a defect occurred which entailed dismantling an inside cylinder connecting rod, the valve gear on the other side of the engine would also be put out of action so that it would be unable to move. In addition, some of the details, particularly the forging combining the quadrant with the oscillating lever, were complicated.[11]

The 990s took part in comparative trials with the Midland three-cylinder compounds, but owing to their short travel valves they could not equal the performance of the latter. If they had had long travel valves the results might have been very different, because the steam circuit of the compounds was not good. [They had a poorer valve gear, for instance, than the three-cylinder compound 4–4–0s of the Great Northern Railway (Ireland), built in 1932.][12]

Trials with the *North Star* showed Churchward that he had at last got an engine that rode as well as the French Atlantics, in addition to being comparable to them in power and economy. He decided therefore to stick to simple expansion. There remained the questions of the wheel and cylinder arrangements. Comparison in service showed the 4–4–2 to be rather freer running and more comfortable in its riding than the 4–6–0, but that the latter had the extra adhesive weight which was invaluable on the steep gradients in the West and in bad weather.[13] Churchward's second decision, therefore, was that all future large express engines should be 4–6–0s. As regards the relative advantages of two or four cylinders, Churchward thought that more experience was needed. Ten more 4–6–0s of each kind were therefore ordered. The two-cylinder engines had names starting with *Saint* (conferring on all the two-cylinder variety the class name of Saint) and the four-cylinder engines (with cylinder dimensions increased slightly to a diameter of 14¼ inches) had names ending with *Star*, which similarly gave the class name to all the four-cylinder 4–6–0s.

The final decision was made as a result of experience in 1907. The locomotive inspectors expressed the opinion that the *Stars* were a coach better than the *Saints* on fast trains of from twelve to fourteen coaches, and they ascribed this to the smoother riding and the shorter cut-offs possible with the Walschaerts gear. On the other hand, the *Saints* were better at getting away from stops, though the pull that they could exert was limited by the necessity of stopping the explosive exhaust from pulling the fire about. Indeed, above a speed of 40 m.p.h. the maximum cut-off had to be limited to 40 per cent.[14]

Churchward decided that the *Saints* were to be the normal express engines, but that a limited number of the more expensive *Stars* should be built for heavy non-stop trains running at high speed. They would run more smoothly, and he believed that under these conditions they would make up their higher first cost by running a greater mileage between general repairs than the *Saints*.[15]

The fierce exhaust of the *Saints* posed something of a problem. Churchward had an idea that reservoirs in communication with the exhaust passages might soften and prolong the beats, and Holcroft was instructed to examine this possibility; but, having produced a simple method of doing this, it was found that it made no appreciable difference.[16] Chapelon comments that Hedley had tried the same thing in 1811, but with similar lack of success![17] Eventually a solution was found in the 'jumper' top to the blast pipe, which lifted to give increased area for the exhaust at cut-offs over 40 per cent. This allowed an engine to work hard at starting without disturbing the fire unduly.[18]

Chapelon thinks it a pity that Churchward did not tumble on the simple solution that he found so successful on simple expansion engines with long travel valves and a fierce blast. He so shaped the ports in the piston valve liners that as they opened they offered a decreasing section to the exhaust. This was first used very effectively in his rebuild of Etat 2-8-2 No. 141.E.113. Its effectiveness was shown in a rather unexpected manner when he applied the same treatment to one of the PLM 140.J class 2-8-0s, which had an unenviable reputation for throwing their fires out of the chimney. By a mistake the valve liners were put in the wrong way round so that the ports offered a decreasing section to the admission of live steam, and so throttled it that power was decreased and consumption increased, whilst the exhaust beats became more violent than ever! However, when the mistake was found and rectified the remedy proved perfectly satisfactory.[19]

The various tests and comparisons discussed in this chapter were probably the most important ever carried out in the history of the British steam locomotive; for as a result of them the 4-6-0 with two outside cylinders eventually became the most widely used of all passenger and mixed traffic engines for main line services on British railways, the multi-cylinder simple expansion six-coupled locomotive was gradually adopted for the heaviest express passenger duties, and, with the notable exceptions of the Midland and Great Northern (Ireland) 4-4-0s, compounding in the British Isles came to a virtual end.

But why did the finest compounds in the world fail to show any marked superiority over Churchward's simples? It is this perhaps which puzzled Rous-Marten; for in his above-quoted article he says that de Glehn told him in a letter that the idea underlying compounding was the more economical employment of a given supply of steam. Other French engineers wrote to him in similar fashion. Baudry of the PLM said, 'There is no saving of coal for a certain work performed, but there is more work for the same coal consumption. Du Bousquet wrote, 'The same quantity of steam is generated, but the useful effect is greater.' And Moffre of the Midi said that in comparison with simple engines the compounds 'haul with a slightly less coal consumption much heavier trains by about forty per cent'. And yet here was Churchward apparently refuting the opinions of four of the most eminent engineers of the day.

The Atlantics embodied partially, but not fully, the proportions established by Barbier in the experiments referred to in Chapter 7. Whether or not Churchward was aware of the results of these experiments is not known; but he went further than du Bousquet towards implementing the ideal proportions suggested. There was a further factor: the 'double valve' variable exhaust fitted to the Atlantics did not favour the ideal circuit and economical running.[20] With skilled use it was satisfactory; but if the adjustment was used to narrow the blast pipe with a view to increasing the speed of the steam jet entraining the firebox gases, the back pressure on the pistons could be so increased that the work done by the steam in the cylinders was badly reduced—and away would go all the economic advantages of compounding. Various modifications of these engines were tried by Churchward, but there does not seem to be a record as to whether or not a Great Western No. 1 boiler and fixed exhaust improved their performance, and, as Chapelon says, it is a pity that the comparative running on the Great Western was not subjected to a deeper analysis.[21] As a start was made in fitting them with the No. 1 boiler in August 1907, it is possible that Rous-Marten's article was based, partly at any rate, on experiences with such a modified Atlantic.

Meanwhile in France du Bousquet found that he was needing more adhesion than he would get with the Atlantics, and because this great man was the only locomotive engineer of the time who could compare with Churchward, it is worthwhile describing how he tackled the problem. At that time the Nord main lines were being strengthened to take an axle weight of 18 tons, but on certain stretches 16 tons was still the maximum allowed. The adhesion of the Atlantics was becoming insufficient for the heaviest expresses and du Bousquet decided that he must have a 4-6-0, but one with an axle load of 16 tons to enable it to run over all the main lines. He would need the Atlantic boiler, but this would entail cutting weight by reducing the size of the coupled wheels. In 1896 the Midi had put into service their 1301 class of mixed traffic four cylinder 4–6–0s with 5 foot 8 inch coupled wheels and the de Glehn compound arrangement. These were derived from some similar locomotives designed by the *Société Alsacienne* for the Baden State Railways in 1893. The Midi engines were so successful that they were adopted by the P–O, the Nord, and the Etat, and by railways in Germany, China, and Spain. The Nord series of these useful engines was known as the 3100 class. Du Bousquet decided to take them as a basis and to make up for their small wheels by increasing the ports by 30 per cent in the high pressure cylinders and by 25 per cent in the low pressure cylinders. In fact this was not quite enough. Chapelon points out that the port areas of the Atlantic would need to be multiplied first by the ratio of the smaller coupled wheels to the larger, which was 1.17, and then by the ratio of the new cylinder diameters to the old. He then shows by calculation that this would have produced port areas of 20 in.^{2} high pressure and 36 in.^{2} low pressure, whereas the actual values established were 19 in.^{2} high pressure and 32 in.^{2} low pressure. The difference, however, was not very great and, fitted with the Atlantic boiler, these 3513 class 4–6–0s could run at the French legal maximum speed of 75 m.p.h. nearly as easily as the Atlantics with their 6 foot 8½ inch coupled wheels; whilst the 3100 class mixed traffic engines, from which they were drived, could only reach 56 m.p.h.[22] However, Chapelon thinks that du Bousquet could have done better. The port area/cylinder cross section ratios were 1:7.9 high pressure and 1:11.4 low pressure, and in a letter to the author he says: 'These figures were still in my opinion not good enough and should have been closer to a ratio of 1:5.' Nevertheless du Bousquet had produced an excellent locomotive which was, in its way, as much a landmark in French locomotive development as was Churchward's No. 40 in British development. For, just as all subsequent Great Western four-cylinder engines and the first Pacifics of the London Midland & Scottish stemmed from the *North Star*, so did the design of the famous *Superpacifics* of the Nord follow the design principles of No. 3513; and the remarkable results obtained by these precedents inspired the P–O to try rebuilding its own Pacifics. It was this decision which enabled Chapelon to go very much further on the same path in his brilliant rebuilding of P–O Pacific No. 3566.[23]

Du Bousquet described his new engines and their performance in the August 1909 edition of the *Revue Générale des Chemins de Fer*. Churchward doubtless read this account and may well have wished that du

Bousquet's 4–6–0s had been available at the time that he bought the Atlantics. But there could have been no economic justification for buying one at this juncture, when his policy decisions had been made.

Eventually 149 of the 3513 (later 230.D) class were built, construction continuing up till 1913. They were all in time superheated, and when later in their career they were fitted with the Lemaitre exhaust (a Nord variant of Chapelon's Kylchap) their performance became even more phenomenal, and they were hauling express trains until the last days of French steam, and long after all the Atlantics had been scrapped.

Perhaps no locomotive comparative trials would have been more interesting than between Churchward's *Stars* and du Bosquet's 3513s, after both had been superheated; for they were the giants of their day.

NOTES

1 L. M. Vilain, *Un Siècle de Matériel et Traction sur le Réseau d'Orléans* (Paris, A. Gozlan, 1962), p. 112.
2 O. S. Nock, *Sir William Stanier* (London, Ian Allan, 1964), p. 19.
3 H. Holcroft, *An Outline of Great Western Locomotive Practice* (London, Locomotive Publishing Co., 1957), p. 94.
4 C. Rous-Marten, 'Locomotive Practice and Performance', *The Railway Magazine*, **XXII**, pp. 377–9 (May 1908).
5 British Transport Historical Records, GEN 3–62.2.
6 R. F. Hanks, conversation with the author.
7 H. Holcroft, *Locomotive Adventure* (London, Ian Allan), 57–8.
8 W. N. Pellow, letter to the author.
9 E. C. Poultney, *British Express Locomotive Development* (London, George Allen & Unwin, 1952), p. 71.
10 Ibid.
11 Sir William Stanier, 'George Jackson Churchward, Chief Mechanical Engineer, Great Western Railway', *Transactions of the Newcomen Society*, **XXX** (1960).
12 R. C. Bond, conversation with the author.
13 Holcroft, *G. W. Locomotive Practice*, p. 98.
14 A. Chapelon, letter to the author.
15 Holcroft, *G.W. Loco. Practice*, pp. 106–7.
16 Ibid.
17 A. Chapelon, letter to the author.
18 Holcroft, *G.W. Loco. Practice*, p. 107.
19 A. Chapelon, letter to the author.
20 Ibid.
21 Ibid.
22 Ibid.
23 A. Chapelon, *La Locomotive à Vapeur* (Paris, J. B. Bailliere et Fils, 1952), p. 142.

Chapter 10

The Great Bear

Probably no locomotive in history has excited so much speculation about the reason for its design and construction as has No. 111 *The Great Bear*, the first of the Pacific type in Great Britain. G. J. Church-ward, great autocrat that he was, does not seem to have told anybody why, when construction of his four-cylinder *Stars* had started so recently, he should want to build this single 4–6–2 locomotive, with an axle weight which was above the maximum permitted on the principal main lines. Not that his reticence was unusual, for it does not appear that he was in the habit of giving reasons for his decisions. Normally he would first state what he intended to do and then listen to opinions on the best way of doing it. When he had made up his mind, he would send for the Chief Draughtsman, G. H. Burrows, and give him an outline of the project. Burrows would then select a suitable draughtsman to get a scheme out on the drawing board.

The drawing office staff at that time was divided into gangs, each of which was concerned with particular parts of locomotive design, and in charge of each gang was a leading draughtsman (styled 'chargeman'). When the job was sufficiently far advanced, Churchward would come and sit on the draughtsman's stool, with, grouped around him, Burrows, O. E. F. Deverell (Assistant Chief Draughtsman), the chargeman of the gang concerned, and the draughtsman entrusted with the task. He would then listen while Burrows explained to him, point by point, the present situation of the job and how it had developed. When he had finished, Churchward would ask questions and perhaps make suggestions on which he would expect those around him to comment. As a result of the discussion he might want opinions on the practical aspects of the proposals, and would send for the Locomotive Running Superintendent, or the foremen of the shops that would be principally concerned. The matter would then probably be adjourned for a day or two, whilst amendments or different approaches to the scheme were considered in the light of the conclusions reached at the discussion. When Churchward was satisfied that the various courses of action had been fully considered, he would summarise the favourable and adverse aspects of each and make his decision.[1]

We can visualise Churchward, then, sending for Burrows, telling him that he wanted a Pacific and explaining the type of locomotive that he had in mind—but not why he wanted it. (It does not appear that anyone ever had the temerity to ask him, for none of those who worked under him ever knew the reason for the building of *The Great Bear*.)

But perhaps the reason behind the Pacific can be gleaned from the previously mentioned discussion of the paper of 31 March 1903 on *American Locomotive Practice*. In the course of it, Churchward said: 'Probably, to English locomotive engineers, the part of the paper which deals with boilers is the most interesting; especially the reasonably wide firebox which the author has described. An express engine with a similar box has just been put on the Great Northern Railway by Mr Ivatt, and I trust it will have a good trial in England. I think English locomotive engineers are within a reasonable distance of adopting it, and I am sorry that the French "Atlantic" engine, which is to be put on the Great Western Railway is not fitted with it—but I am taking the engine as it stands.' (It is apparent that, to this sturdy Devonian, 'England' signified the whole of the British Isles, and that he did not think that the Celtic extremities needed separate mention!) The point in Churchward's statement that merits particular attention is that he thought English locomotive engineers to be 'within measurable distance' of adopting the wide firebox, and that must have included himself. His disappointment that the French Atlantics had not got the wide firebox shows that he very much wanted to try it. But, in accordance with his customary cautious approach, any trials would be very lengthy and thorough before he came to a conclusion that big engines with wide fireboxes would or would not be suitable for the Great Western. Anyhow, as soon as he was satisfied that he had designed express locomotives that were adequate for all Great Western needs for some years ahead, he decided to experiment with a wide firebox. There arose, then, the question as to the most suitable type of engine. It would obviously have to have a trailing truck because the firebox could not spread over big coupled wheels. An Atlantic would do, but he had already concluded that a four-coupled engine had not got sufficient adhesion to work heavy express trains over the more difficult routes. In any case, he had to look ahead to the time when the *Stars* would be stretched and more power would be needed. (K. J. Cook, indeed, has always believed that *The Great Bear* represented a quest for more power.[2]) The engine, therefore, would have to be a Pacific. With the very big engine that was emerging from his thoughts, there might be a problem in axle loading. At that time the principal main lines of the Great Western were limited to an axle load of 20 tons, and the big boiler that would be necessary to supply the power he wanted would probably bring the axle weight above this. On the other hand, Churchward knew that J. C. (later Sir James) Inglis, when Chief Engineer of the Great Western, had in 1902 initiated a project to strengthen these lines to carry 22 tons. He was then on friendly terms with Churchward and there must have been discussion between them. (Later, after Inglis became General Manager in 1903, considerable hostility arose between these two strong personalities, owing to Churchward's opposition to attempts by Inglis to bring the Locomotive Superintendent under the General Manager, so depriving the former of his direct access to the Board. Perhaps as a legacy of this hostility, the General Managers after Inglis and the Chief Mechanical Engineers were never informed officially that strengthening of the track had been carried out. In fact it never came out into the open until Churchward's successor, Collett, said to the then General Manager, Sir Felix Pole, 'If I could have an axle load of $22\frac{1}{2}$ tons I would give you a very fine locomotive.' As a result of Collett's statement, the then Chief Civil Engineer was asked what axle loading he was providing for, and then the astonishing fact was revealed that for over twenty-two years work had been going on to raise the $19\frac{1}{2}$ ton limit to 22 tons. In the light of the progress already made it was possible to give Collett authority to go ahead with the *King* class of 1927.[3]) Churchward must have known that the line between Paddington and Bristol was ready to carry his projected Pacific. In addition, he probably reckoned that by the time he had finished the very extensive tests he had in mind, the route to Plymouth might be ready and perhaps also that to Birmingham. He could not foresee that plans for both tests and track improvement would be upset by the outbreak of war in 1914. (W. N. Pellow points out, however, that the improvement of the main lines was a very slow process, and that as far as he is aware no special Board grants were made to hurry up the process.[4])

Apart from the advantages to be derived from a large grate area, Churchward was probably alive to the dependence of his engines, with their long narrow fireboxes, on high grade fuel. In a letter to the author, referring to his experiences during the Second World War and after, W. N. Pellow writes: 'The quality of coal supplied for loco use got gradually worse and worse, and I found on inquiry that the Pacifics of other regions, with their wider, shallower fireboxes were reported to be doing very well on the inferior fuel; while our firemen, with the long deep fireboxes of our standard boilers, had considerable difficulties with this fuel.' Pellow, as Locomotive Running Superintendent of the Great Western, was the person most concerned with the problem.

F. W. Hawksworth, who later succeeded Collett as Chief Mechanical Engineer, was the draughtsman entrusted with the general arrangement drawing of the Pacific locomotive which was to be *The Great Bear*.[5] H. Holcroft, who was then in the cylinder gang, was given the task of getting out the drawings for the cylinders. Churchward had said that there was to be no departure from the *Star* class arrangement, other than an increase in cylinder diameter. The diameter was limited, however, by various factors. The longer wheelbase increased the bogie side movement; but the trailing bogie wheels were behind the outside cylinders, giving little clearance, and there was not much clearance between the leading bogie wheels and the inside cylinders. Holcroft found, therefore, that a diameter of 15 inches was the practical limit. On Churchward's next visit Holcroft told him this, but added that if the tyres were reduced from the standard Great Western width of $5\frac{3}{4}$ inches to $5\frac{1}{4}$ inches, as used on most other railways, the cylinder diameter could be increased to 16 inches. However, Churchward would not agree to this modification, and seemed quite happy with 15 inch cylinders. It was no doubt the increased boiler power in which he was primarily interested. Holcroft points out that this use of a large boiler with a wide firebox and a large grate area, in conjunction with relatively small cylinders, was a reversion to the broad-gauge practice of having a large reserve of boiler power. This should ensure a higher possible average speed than with the *Stars*, because the reserve of power could be used to allow of faster running on rising gradients.[6]

The big Standard No. 6 boiler was the principal feature of the engine. Holcroft says that Churchward spent a lot of time on its development, and that it was carried out on the board of W. L. Watson (known as 'Scotty' because he came to Swindon from the Great North of Scotland Railway). Only one ring of the boiler barrel was coned; the wide firebox was, as one would expect, of the Belpaire pattern; and the grate area was 41·8 ft². Churchward would not have an intermediate combustion chamber because of the trouble that had been experienced with it in the *Krugers*, and, as he did not 'set in' the smokebox tubeplate, the boiler tubes had the exceptional length of 23 feet, and were consequently given a diameter of $2\frac{1}{2}$ inches to compensate, instead of the 2 inches of the

Stars.[7] Churchward has indeed been criticised for the length of these tubes, but the whole boiler design had been very carefully worked out. In the above-mentioned paper on *Large Locomotive Boilers* Churchward said: 'The ratio of diameter to length of the tube undoubtedly has a most important bearing upon the steaming qualities of the boiler and upon the efficiency of the heat absorption.' In fact, once the firemen got used to the wide grate, the steaming quality of the boiler proved excellent.

The radial truck, with its inside bearings, was probably the one really weak point of the engine. The axleboxes were difficult to lubricate efficiently and their surfaces were in a position where dust from the ashpans and grit thrown up from the track could reach them. The result was frequent overheating.[8] On the other hand, the bogie was excellent, for *The Great Bear* was the first engine to be fitted with the de Glehn bogie, which subsequently became standard on the Great Western, the London Midland & Scottish, and British Railways.[9]

While *The Great Bear* was still being tested, W. N. Pellow came to the Swindon drawing office. He had started his service with the Great Western in May 1904 at the St Blazey Works and sheds in Cornwall as an apprentice in engine-turning, fitting, and erecting. As Pellow is a Cornishman (as indeed is the author), St Blazey, the headquarters of the old Cornwall Minerals Railway, was a very suitable starting point. There were still a number of machines in the machine shop, so that he got early experience of boring and drilling, lathework, planing, and shaping machines. With these, quite heavy overhauls were undertaken on the fleet of 0–6–0 tank engines based on the area. In 1908 Pellow was transferred to Swindon Works to finish his apprenticeship under Churchward, and he immediately took advantage of the opportunities offered there for technical education. He did well and, as a result, he entered the Swindon drawing office early in 1912.

In the drawing office a small team of men had been built up, known as the 'Experimental Gang', whose principal task was to ride on locomotives in service, observing the effects of various experiments and reporting on them to Churchward. For Churchward, says Pellow, was very cautious and would not put any ideas or schemes or a new engine into general use until proved in practice over a period of general working. The prototype of a new engine or carriage, for instance, was tested under all kinds of service conditions before he would recommend to the Board that a number of such a type should be put into service. When Pellow went to the drawing office the Experimental Gang were still busy watching and experimenting with *The Great Bear* and submitting their findings to an intensely interested Churchward.[10] These lengthy tests were brought to an untimely end by the outbreak of the First World War, and before normal conditions could be resumed on the railways Churchward had retired.

Unfortunately, records of the various trials do not seem to have survived. 'Teething' troubles there were, as one might expect with such a revolutionary engine. Until firemen found the correct way to deal with the unfamiliar wide firebox there were complaints about steaming. R. F. Hanks, who was a premium apprentice at Swindon at the time, says that the engine spent a lot of time in the Works having various devices tried in connection with the trailing axle, and that she was much given to derailing when traversing sharp curves in the engine shed yards. 'But,' he adds, 'we loved her and very often I would go up to Swindon station to see her go through on a Bristol express at about 8 p.m.'[11] *The Great Bear* worked all sorts of trains between Bristol and Paddington, from express passenger to fast goods. The late J. N. Maskelyne mentions an occasion in 1909 when the engine left Swindon with a fast goods train weighing no less than 2375 tons, which it hauled non-stop to Acton at an average speed of 24·5 m.p.h.[12]

The axle load of *The Great Bear* was, after sundry re-adjustments, 20 tons 9 hundredweight per coupled axle, which was above the limit at the time for any line other than that between Paddington and Bristol.[13] Churchward would no doubt have dearly loved to see his great Pacific working over a much wider range; for, when shortly before his retirement he heard that Gresley was building a Pacific, he said (according to a tale which Pellow says 'went the rounds'): 'Gresley could have had our *Bear* to play with if only we had known in time.' Indeed, the lessons that could have been learned from running *The Great Bear* on the Great Northern main line would have been invaluable to both companies. Gresley might have adopted Churchward's long travel valves from the start and Collett might have built Pacifics; and the exchange between the Great Western *Castle* and the Gresley Pacific would probably never have taken place.

The end of this famous and fascinating engine is recorded in the following extraordinary minute of a meeting of the Locomotive Committee on 1 May 1924:

'Engine 111 "The Great Bear" Reconstruction

'The above engine was built at Swindon in February 1908, and had a tractive effort of 27,800 lbs and weighed 142 tons 15 cwt.

35 Four-cylinder 4–6–0 No. 4006 *Red Star* on the Great Western Royal train of 1907, near Chippenham on 20 July 1907. (*British Railways*)

36 29 October 1905. The new Postal Train, headed by Atlantic No. 183 (later named *Red Gauntlet*). (*British Railways*)

37 *Star* class 4–6–0 No. 4038 *Queen Philippa* on 15 August 1915 at Rushey Platt with an ambulance train composed of *Toplight* carriages. (*British Railways*)

The Cornish Riviera Express on 8 August 1922, composed of *Toplight* stock and the first train to be painted in the re-introduced chocolate and cream. The train is headed by one of the *Abbey* series of *Star* class locomotives, still in its original austerity livery with cast iron chimney (*British Railways*)

Pacific No. 111 *The Great Bear*. (*British Railways*)

40 *The Great Bear* fitted with top feed. (*British Railways*)

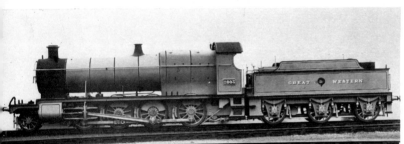

41 Two-cylinder 2–8–0 heavy goods locomotive No. 2803. (*British Railways*)

42 *Saint* class two-cylinder 4–6–0 No. 2934 *Butleigh Court*, with the Holcroft curves. (*British Railways*)

43 2–6–0 mixed traffic locomotive No. 4303. (*British Railways*)

'Owing to its extreme weight, it was necessary for the Hanwell Viaduct [a pencilled correction in the margin says: 'the old iron skew bridge over the Uxbridge Road—not the viaduct'] to be rebuilt before the engine could be allowed to work between London and Bristol, to which route it has been limited the whole 16 years on account of the enormous expenditure that would be necessary to strengthen the bridges to carry it on other main line routes. Mr. Grierson has estimated the cost of doing what would be necessary at over £500,000. The "Castle" class of four-cylinder engine has now been produced and proved successful, the engines of which have a greater tractive effort than "The Great Bear" by 13¾% viz. 31,625 lbs., and as they only weigh 119 tons 17 cwt., or 22 tons 18 cwts. less than "The Great Bear", no alterations are necessary to any of the bridges. There is, therefore, no longer any reason for the continued existence of "The Great Bear" and as it recently came into the shops for general repair and needed new cylinders and a new boiler, advantage has been taken of the occasion to reconstruct it, so that it will be similar to one of the "Castle" type.

'In the past, reconstructions of engines have been dealt with in the same way as repairs and have not been reported to the Directors, but it is thought desirable to do so in this case owing to the notoriety of the engine and to the fact that several other British railways followed our example in adopting the Pacific type and are still building them. They have not produced a more powerful engine of less weight.'[14]

Collett must bear ultimate responsibility for this misleading and inaccurate document. No competent engineer would assess the relative power of express locomotives on the basis of their starting tractive efforts; and it is questionable, to say the least, as to whether a *Castle* could have put up the same performance as *The Great Bear* on the heavy train mentioned above. The statement that several British railways were building Pacific locomotives was quite untrue. Only two had built them, the Great Northern and the North Eastern, and by 1924 only the Great Northern type was still being built (for the London & North Eastern Railway). Finally, as three years later the principal main lines could take the *King* class with a 22½-ton axle load, it is clear that the statement about the enormous expenditure necessary to strengthen bridges was false, and that Grierson, the Chief Engineer, must either have been withholding information or had been incorrectly briefed by his own department.

There may have been a case for scrapping *The Great Bear*, but it is not contained in the above minute; and there must be a suspicion that Collett wanted to get rid of the engine and that any excuse would do. He may well have considered its continued existence beside his brand new *Castles* to be an embarrassment. Churchward was fond of *The Great Bear* and was very upset when he learned of the destruction of his engine.[15]

It could well be that *The Great Bear* needed modification, but the intensive testing that had been carried out should have produced sufficient data for the design of a new generation of Pacifics. But Collett did not have that spark of genius which animated his great predecessor. Under his régime Swindon continued to build engines which were clearly Churchward in design and were therefore excellent; but there was no real technical advance on the locomotives of 1906, and so Great Western pre-eminence in design was gradually lost.

NOTES

1 H. Holcroft, *An Outline of Great Western Locomotive Practice* (London, Locomotive Publishing Co., 1957), pp. 96–7.
2 K. J. Cook, letter to the author.
3 Felix J. C. Pole, *His Book* (Town and Country Press, Bracknell, 1968), pp. 87–8.
4 W. N. Pellow, letter to the author.
5 O. S. Nock, *The Great Western Railway in the Twentieth Century* (London, Ian Allan, 1964), p. 109.
6 Holcroft, op. cit., p. 120.
7 Holcroft, *Locomotive Adventure* (London, Ian Allan), p. 60.
8 Holcroft, *G.W. Loco. Practice*, p. 121.
9 *The Railway Magazine*, **XXX**, p. 438 (May 1908).
10 W. N. Pellow, letter to the author.
11 R. F. Hanks, letter to the author.
12 J. N. Maskelyne, *Model Railway News* (February 1947).
13 Holcroft, *G.W. Loco. Practice*, p. 121.
14 British Transport Historical Records, GEN 3–62–6.
15 O. S. Nock, *The G.W.R. Stars, Castles, & Kings, Part I* (Newton Abbot, David & Charles, 1967), p. 90.

Chapter 11

The Churchward Régime

In previous chapters we have considered the development of Churchward's prototype locomotives and his arrival at a policy. This chapter deals with the locomotives which were built to implement that policy, the various modifications to the original designs, and some brief mention of carriages and wagons.

LOCOMOTIVES—STANDARD AND OTHERWISE

In 1904 the first order was placed for locomotives for which Churchward was, officially at any rate, responsible. Rather oddly, perhaps, the order was for ten of the small 2–6–2 tank engines with 4 foot 1½ inch coupled wheels, similar to the prototype, No. 115. Design had been carried out at Swindon, but the order was placed with the Stafford Road Works at Wolverhampton, which were in need of new work at the time and which were not suitable for the construction of large engines. Initially these 2–6–2 tanks were numbered 3101 to 3110, but they were later numbered in the 44xx series. After construction they were tried out on numerous branch lines in Devon, Cornwall, and South Wales, where route restrictions prohibited the use of larger engines. For a number of years they did good work, hauling both passenger and goods trains over severe gradients. From a running and maintenance point of view, wheel flange wear over the sharp curves of these branch lines caused something of a problem.[1]

As a result of experience it was considered that they would be more generally useful if their coupled wheels were rather larger. A further twenty were therefore built at Wolverhampton in 1906–08 with 4 foot 7½ inch coupled wheels and slightly larger cylinders. They were the first of a class which, numbered 45xx, eventually consisted of 175 very useful branch-line engines.[2]

The next order, also in 1904, was for ten of the larger general-purpose tank engines with 5 foot 8 inch coupled wheels, similar to No.

99. They were built at Swindon and heralded a long line, though from 1908 engines of this class were fitted with the Standard No. 4 boiler instead of the No. 2.[3] As the years went by there were various modifications. Their construction continued long after Churchward retired until there were 266 of them.

In 1905 the outside cylinder 4–4–0s, identical with the prototype of 1904 were running on the Shrewsbury and Hereford line. Later, in addition to this section, they worked for many years between Wolverhampton and both Chester and Oxford. Pellow had much experience on them during the years 1924–29 when he was Assistant Divisional Superintendent at Wolverhampton. They would roll, he says, quite a bit at speed and were known locally as 'Churchward's Rough Riders'; but they did a lot of useful work on the old Northern Division.[4] They were named after English and Welsh counties and were designated the *County*, or 38xx, class. They were followed by a 4–4–2 tank version, inevitably nicknamed the 'County Tanks', but which differed from the tender engines in having the Standard No. 2 boiler instead of the No. 4. They were used largely on services in and out of London as far as Reading and Oxford on fast 'commuter' services, and could work up quite a good speed between their frequent stops.[5] There were eventually forty of the *Counties* and thirty of the *County Tanks*. Some years later, in 1913, there was a single very pretty little 4–4–2 tank engine with 5 foot 8 inch wheels (instead of the 6 foot 8½ inch wheels of the bigger engines), which was intended as the precursor of some passenger engines for Cornwall. R. F. Hanks watched her being built and admired her. But the operators could not find a niche for her and she was not repeated.[6]

The *Counties* were followed shortly by the admirable 2–8–0 heavy goods engines, similar to the prototype No. 97. These hauled the Great Western heavy freight trains until the last days of steam; and, including those built after Churchward's retirement, the class eventually numbered 167.

Whilst Swindon was busy building all these standard types with two outside cylinders and many common parts, Holcroft was surprised that twenty more double-framed inside cylinder engines of the *Atbara* type were ordered. They were called the *Flower* class and had the No. 2 boiler, instead of the No. 4 of the *Cities*, so that their axle loads would be light enough to work over a wide range of routes. Holcroft was told that the reason for their construction was that more engines were needed for secondary services and that Churchward, who had been busy providing suitable locomotives for main-line traffic, had not yet decided what he would have for secondary use. The *Flower* class were followed by fifteen double-framed engines similar to the *Bulldogs* and called the *Bird* class. Both *Flowers* and *Birds* differed from the earlier engines of their respective types in having the de Glehn pattern bogie.[7]

The four-cylinder 4–6–0s came out in a series of batches with different 'type' names. Thus, whilst the class as a whole was designated *Star*, the particular batch to which a locomotive belonged could be readily identified by its name. The first lot with names ending with 'Star', e.g. *North Star*, were delivered in May 1907. In March 1908 came the *Knights*, e.g. *Knight of the Garter*, the first series to be built with the de Glehn bogie. In 1909 a series named after the Kings of England appeared, though the names had no numerical suffix, e.g. *King Edward*. (When the later *King* class were built in 1927, the earlier *Kings* were given names ending with 'Monarch', e.g. *King Edward* became *British Monarch*, and *King James* became *Dutch Monarch*—a change that the second James would hardly have appreciated!) The next batch of 1910 were, logically, *Queens*, e.g. *Queen Mary*—the first of the series because King George V had just ascended the throne.

The next 4–6–0s were more of the two-cylinder *Saint* class, named after 'Courts', which were built in 1911 and 1912. (It is of some interest that the name of the first of these, *Arlington Court*, was partly repeated in the name of the first of the 5 foot 8 inch wheel *Grange* class 4–6–0s, *Arlington Grange*, built in 1936.)

In 1913 there was a change of policy, and it was decided that all future 4–6–0 express engines should have four cylinders. Ten more *Courts* had actually been ordered, but as a result of this decision only five were built and the remaining five were completed as four-cylinder *Star* class engines and given the names of the five princes who were the sons of King George V, e.g. *Prince of Wales*, *Prince Albert*. They were followed by another batch of *Stars* named after princesses, e.g. *Princess Mary*.[8]

The last *Stars*, though ordered whilst Churchward was still Chief Mechanical Engineer, came out in 1922 and 1923 after he had retired. In appearance they reflected the economies introduced during the First World War, for they had plain tapered cast iron chimneys and no brass beading on the edges of their splashers. All the same, they had an attractive appearance of their own, and a coloured picture of *Glastonbury Abbey* (for they were all named after Abbeys) adorned at the time the author's bedroom wall.

In August 1907 a step had been taken to bring the French Atlantics more into line with Great Western practice by equipping one of them with an unsuperheated Swindon No. 1 boiler, together with a fixed blast pipe instead of the Nord variable type. At the same time the vertical out-side steam pipes from the top of the boiler barrel were replaced by horizontal outside pipes from the smokebox. This alteration would have in any case been necessary when, as happened later, the engines were given superheated boilers. The arrangement in fact was very similar to that adopted on the Nord when their Atlantics were superheated. Hol-croft, during his time in the Testing Section, noted that the highest drawbar horsepower recorded in the dynamometer car was with one of these French compounds with a Swindon superheated boiler. How-ever, this was obtained between 40 and 45 m.p.h., and there was noth-ing to show that it was any better than a *Star* at the higher piston speeds.[9] Rous-Marten would not, perhaps, have been surprised by this result.

In 1910 another standard type appeared, a 2–8–0 side tank locomotive that was virtually a tank version of the 2–8–0 heavy freight engine. As it was required to travel over sharper curves than the latter, some sideplay in the trailing coupled wheels was allowed, and Holcroft had to design coupling rods with joints to permit the vertical and horizontal movement of the trailing wheels.[10]

In the summer of 1909 Holcroft paid what was to be a momentous visit to Canada and the United States as one of a party of young engin-eers. He was very impressed with the extensive use made of the 2–6–0 tender type of freight locomotive, with coupled wheels from 4 feet 10 inches to 5 feet in diameter, as a general-purpose engine for secondary services and branch-line trains. On his return to Swindon he was asked to submit a report on anything he had noted which might be of use to the Great Western. He described a number of Translatlantic practices, but emphasised particularly the extensive use of the 2–6–0 type of loco-motive, and suggested that with larger wheels it could meet many requirements in England.

The sequel to this came the following year. Holcroft was told that now that Churchward had completed his standard types for main lines he was considering the types of locomotives needed for the secondary services. He did not want to build any more double-framed engines and was thinking of replacing the *Atbaras, Bulldogs,* and *Aberdares* by broadly similar types but with inside frames. He wanted to retain inside cylinders but with long travel piston valves, 10 inches in diameter, on top of them, instead of slide valves underneath. Holcroft was given the task of working it out, but soon found that it was difficult to fit 10 inch diameter piston valves above the cylinders without encroaching on the smokebox. Churchward's notice was drawn to this difficulty, and at the same time he was told of Holcroft's comments on the use of the 2-6-0 type in North America. A day or two later Churchward, accompanied by the Chief Draughtsman, arrived at Holcroft's board and said to him: 'Very well, then; get me out a 2-6-0 with 5 foot 8 inch wheels, outside cylinders, the No. 4 boiler, and bring in all the standard parts you can.' Holcroft says that this historic pronouncement was a milestone in the history of the locomotive in Great Britain, because it inaugurated the general utility engine.

It took only a few days to outline the new locomotive, and, because few drawings were needed, materials could be requisitioned straight away and an order for twenty engines was placed on the shops. The first of them appeared in 1911, and the whole twenty were soon afterwards in service. They were an immediate success; the running department was delighted with them, for they could be used on any duty, from fast passenger trains to moderately heavy freight trains,[11] and on account of their 17 tons 12 hundredweight axle weight they could be used on all the routes on which the *Atbaras, Bulldogs,* and *Aberdares* (with No. 2 boilers) were permitted, whilst they had the additional power conferred by the No. 4 boiler. Eventually 322 of these engines (the 4300 class) were built, and at one period they were running about 14 per cent of the engine mileage, though they only constituted about 7 per cent of the locomotive stock. In spite of their 5 foot 8 inch wheels they were very fast. It is said that when Collett was considering whether to reduce the diameter of his projected *King* class 4-6-0s below the existing standard for express trains of 6 feet 8½ inches, the non-stop express in which he was travelling from Swindon to Paddington was overtaken on the relief line hauled by a '43'.[12]

Shortly before the decision was taken to build the 2-6-0s, Holcroft was handed a roll of old drawings of a small 0-6-0 saddle tank engine with outside cylinders and Allan straight link motion. Nine engines of this type had belonged to the Cornwall Minerals Railway and had been taken over in 1877 when the Great Western assumed responsibility for working and maintaining that system. They had been designed by F. Trevithick, the Locomotive Superintendent, for the little company's very severe gradients and had been built by Sharp Stewart in 1873. As originally built they had side tanks and no bunkers (a limited supply of coal being carried on top of the tanks) as Trevithick had intended them to work in pairs back to back.[13] They were very useful little engines, particularly as with their wheel base of only 11 feet they could go anywhere that a wagon could. Of them W. N. Pellow says:

'I remember the 0–6–0T engines of the Cornwall Mineral Railway, having worked on repairs to quite a few of them in my early days; although by that time the engines had been re-constructed to work as single units. My father remembered them working as pairs with only a limited supply of fuel and one set of footplate men; but they never made very long journeys on those days. They would haul empty wagons up to various clay pits and bring down loaded ones to St Blazey yard, where trains of clay were made up for despatch to Par Dock or the port of Fowey. They did the work for which they were designed very well. After some years the engines were fitted with extended frames at the rear, which carried a coal bunker, and also with a covered in cab, a buffer beam, buffers, and drawgear; so that they were able to work as single units. Some were sent to other parts of the system and worked on dock lines and in other areas where sharp curves existed.'[14]

Holcroft was told to produce a completely new set of drawings, keeping to the existing patterns and templates, but to bring every detail into line with current Swindon practice. The reason given was that the Cornish engines were getting old and they would need to be replaced by others of similar design because there was no other class on the Great Western that could undertake their duties. The fruit of Holcroft's work was the appearance in 1910 of five little outside cylinder saddle tank engines, numbered 1361–5.[15] There is a sequel in that in 1934 five more, Nos 1366–71, were built, but with pannier tanks instead of side tanks. This is an interesting example (others being the *Birds* and *Flowers*) of Churchward's continuance of earlier types of locomotives which had proved satisfactory for the job. It was another Churchward practice that was followed by his successor.

With the arrival of the 2–6–0s, Churchward had a range of nine types of locomotive which he considered his standard classes. They were the 4–6–2 express engine, of which *The Great Bear* was the solitary example; the four-cylinder 4–6–0 *Stars* for long distance expresses; the two-cylinder 4–6–0 *Saints* for fast trains with several stops; the two-cylinder 4–4–0 *Counties* for passenger trains on the Shrewsbury–Hereford line and in the old Northern Division; the *County Tanks* for the fast London 'commuter' services; the larger 2–6–2 tank engines for short distance general-purpose duties; the 2–8–0 heavy freight engines; the 2–8–0 tank engines for short distance heavy coal traffi; and the 2–6–0 mixed traffic engines.[16]

The small 2–6–2 tank engines were not considered a standard class, though they so revolutionised the working of branch lines in Devon and Cornwall that the variety with 4 foot $7\frac{1}{2}$ inch coupled wheels (the 4500 class) almost forced their way into the standard range through sheer merit. They monopolised the St Ives branch, for instance, until the last days of steam; and at the time of writing No. 4588 is still at work on the Torbay Steam Railway, between Paignton and Kingswear—the last engine of purely Churchward design to remain in regular traffic. In spite of their small wheels the '45s' were fast and could run with ease at 60 m.p.h.

The last of Churchward's designs was a 2–8–0 engine with 5 foot 8 inch coupled wheels. He had been pressed by the traffic officers to provide an engine suitable to run fast with a heavy load; for it had been recently decided to introduce a number of fast freight trains, vacuum fitted throughout, running at 50 m.p.h. Churchward came to the conclusion that an eight-coupled version of the 2–6–0 fitted with a big boiler was the answer, and W. N. Pellow was given the task of drawing the 'General Arrangement' and 'Cross Sections'.[17] The idea for the engine owed much to the success with which *The Great Bear* had worked the fast and heavy vacuum-fitted goods train ('The Cocoa Train') between London and Bristol. However, the 2–8–0 would have to have a far greater route availability than the Pacific. The first engine, No. 4700, was completed in April 1919, and naturally, as a Churchward design, it incorporated as many standard parts as possible. The engine had a No. 1 boiler, though with a lengthened smokebox to give it the same overall length as the larger boiler which it was intended should be fitted as soon as it was ready. This new boiler needed new flanging blocks, which entailed some delay. However, the eight further engines that were built had this new Standard No. 7 boiler right from the start. These big engines were the first, as a class, to be built with outside steam pipes from the smokebox to the cylinders.[18]

In traffic the '47s' were outstandingly successful, and worked a widespread service of express freight trains, mostly at night and with loads of up to seventy vehicles. They were also used on empty stock trains for the traffic department. Nevertheless, the long 20 foot fixed wheel base caused difficulty in negotiating sharp turnouts and curves in some goods and traffic yards, with some consequent limitation in their use, so that no further engines of this class were put into service.[19]

PISTON VALVES

Churchward's difficulties with piston valves were discussed in Chapter 8. In 1906 he read, in the American technical press, a description of a type called the 'semi-plug' piston valve, and he was so impressed with the design that he immediately purchased the rights for its manufacture in the United Kingdom. In this valve the steam rings, for maintaining steam tightness, were expanded to fit the walls of the steam chest when the regulator was opened and were locked in position by wedge locking rings actuated by steam pressure. When the steam was shut off there was nothing to keep the rings in contact with the steam chest walls, so that when the engine was drifting there was practically no wear, and it was consequently very free running.[20] Trouble with piston valves now ceased on Great Western engines, though it was to plague those of other railways for another twenty years.

SUPERHEATING

In 1906 Churchward made his first trial of superheating by fitting a Schmidt fire-tube superheater to the two-cylinder 4–6–0 No. 2901 *Lady Superior*. This type had twenty-four flue tubes and 307 ft.^{2} of superheater surface, and was the first fire-tube superheater to be used in the United Kingdom. The following year No. 4010 *Western Star* was provided with the American Cole superheater with eighteen flue tubes and 265 ft^2 of superheater surface. Based on the Cole superheater, a Swindon pattern was now designed with 300 ft.^{2} of heating surface, and in 1908 the new No. 4011 *Knight of the Garter* was fitted with it. In the same year *The Great Bear* also received this Swindon No. 1 superheater. In the light of experience modifications were introduced, resulting in the Swindon No. 2 superheater with 275 ft.^{2} with which No. 2922 *Saint Gabriel* was equipped later in 1908. Further improvements led to the Swindon No. 3 superheater, which became the standard pattern, and which was fitted in 1909 to No. 2913 *Saint Andrew* and No. 4021 *King Edward*. It had fourteen flue tubes and 248 ft.^{2} of superheater surface. The surface area was smaller than in the earlier types because Churchward's aim was to raise the temperature of the steam no more than was required to ensure dry steam at the exhaust.[21]

Churchward has been much criticised for his use of a low degree of superheat. But at this period oils had not been developed sufficiently to stand very high temperatures. The contemporary superheated loco-motives of the London & Northern Western Railway worked at a steam temperature of 650°F, as compared with the approximate 550°F of the Great Western.[22] In a letter to the author, R. A. Riddles writes that he first encountered superheating when he was an apprentice at Crewe, in the *Princes* and *Georges*. He adds: 'I remember the trouble we had with carbonisation in the early days, with valve rings being seized up, etc., and carbon having to be chipped out of the valve chests. A snifting valve was fitted to open when coasting; but as the oil quality improved this was done away with, for such a cure was almost as bad as the disease!' Riddles believes that Churchward, realising the likelihood of the oil carbonising and having the advantage of superior Welsh coal, wisely pursued a cautious policy. 'In any case,' he says, 'the Great Western locomotives were far and away better than most, so why invite trouble? The real culprits were his successors who should have realised the bene-fit of higher superheat with the advent of improved oils.' This opinion is endorsed by H. M. Le Fleming in his comments on K. J. Cook's paper.[23] He doubted whether oils for use with highly superheated steam had been developed to a fully satisfactory stage for everyday use, and said that to the best of his recollection, during the period 1921–25, Great Western engines did not suffer the heavy carbonisation often encoun-tered on other lines. He thought that, in the conditions of the past, the Swindon superheater was probably the most practicable all-round type in use.

It is said that Stanier, in the light of his experiences on the LMS, suggested to Collett that it might be worth trying a higher degree of superheat on Great Western engines, but that Collett never replied to his letter. Indeed it is remarkable that the standards established by Churchward were apparently considered sancrosanct, even by a suc-cessor who disliked him, and most of them were never changed during the whole of the Great Western's separate existence. Yet, having regard to Churchward's constant interest in development, it seems probable that, if he had remained as Chief Mechanical Engineer, he would have adopted in due course a higher degree of superheat.

THE DE GLEHN BOGIE

In replacement of the Dean suspension bogie, Churchward had adopted one of American pattern, controlled by swing links, allowing lateral movement to the bogie. It was not entirely satisfactory, and various modifications which were tried did not result in any marked improvement. However, as the bogies on the French Atlantics were proving remarkably successful in service, one of the Swindon-type bogies was converted to the French design, in which weight was carried on side beams attached to the main frames. The improvement effected by this conversion was so marked that the second ten *Star* class engines were built with this bogie, as was also *The Great Bear*, and conversion sets were made so that all existing engines could have their bogies altered as they passed through the shops.[24] When Churchward decided to build his *Flower* class version of the *Atbaras*, Holcroft's part was to re-design the Dean suspension bogie so that it was converted to the de Glehn type. The *Bird* series of the *Bulldogs* also got this bogie.[25]

The de Glehn bogie was later adopted first by the Southern Railway, then by the London Midland & Scottish, and finally by British Railways.

TOP FEED

The point of entry of the feed water on Great Western engines had varied in the past, but in the later Dean period the clack boxes were situated on the sides of the barrel towards the smokebox end, and a long exterior pipe took the feed water from the injectors below the footplate to the clacks. In Churchward's standard boilers the pair of clack boxes were fixed to the bottom of the barrel near the smokebox end. They were carried by a casting fixed to the barrel having a common vertical uptake. The outlet in the boiler was partially covered by a hood which directed the incoming feed water along the bottom of the barrel towards the front of the firebox. This arrangement worked well, but there were instances of barrel plates in contact with the incoming feed being pitted for several feet from the inlet towards the rear. This pitting could develop into more serious corrosion, penetrating deeper into the metal and widening. The trouble was attributed to the oxygen of the air, dissolved in the feed water, being liberated again by contact with the hot barrel and attacking the steel.

Churchward decided that the best way of tackling the problem was to expose the incoming feed water to the steam in the boiler above the water level, and from this idea he developed his 'top feed' arrangement. It was apparent that this would have the additional advantage that any lime (producing temporary hardness in the feed water) would be precipitated by the expulsion of carbon dioxide, so that the impurity would descend as sludge, rather than forming scale on the hot metal surfaces.

The cover over the manhole, carrying the safety valves, was replaced by a new casting with flanges on each side for attachment to the two clack boxes. Inside the boiler were two trays, each 4 feet long, placed on each side of the main steam pipe to the regulator and carried on the longitudinal pair of stays in the boiler. From the clack boxes the feed water was discharged into a ducting and led to the trays. These had serrated edges, and the feed water, overflowing through the serrations, fell in small streams along the boiler.

This system was introduced in 1911 and resulted in a considerable reduction in the cost of maintenance, for there was no marked fall in temperature in any particular spot. In addition, steam pressure was more easily maintained on a long run.

When all the standard boilers had been dealt with, top feed was extended to older boilers. In the case of those which had a dome containing a regulator, a separate mounting was placed on top of the barrel and in advance of the dome, to carry the two clack boxes.[26] (An arrangement which was later revived by Stanier on his LMS boilers.)

LUBRICATION AND BRAKES

A noteworthy introduction was the sight-feed lubricator, which enabled the driver to see from the footplate how oil was being fed to each cylinder and to the regulator valve while the engine was in motion, and also permitted him to vary the individual feed as required. 'This,' says Pellow, 'was a great improvement on the old "hit and miss" arrangement.'[27]

In about 1911 it was apparent that the standard brake application valve and ejector with single cone was becoming inadequate, due to the development of the locomotive and consequent increase in its loading capacity; for not only had trains become longer, but most of the new large coaches had two cylinders. However, it appears that the immediate need for an improved brake was shown by incidents such as the pulling of the communication cord in the middle of the Severn tunnel and other places where a stop was inadvisable. The four-cone ejector was accordingly designed. This was in two parts; the portion housing the valves, which was mounted on the firebox front, and the ejector proper which was fitted on the right outside of the firebox. One steam valve, known as the small ejector, controlled only one of the cones, while the other steam valve controlled the remaining three cones. The single cone was intended to maintain vacuum while the train was standing or to assist the vacuum pump, if necessary, while running. Three, or four, cones could be used

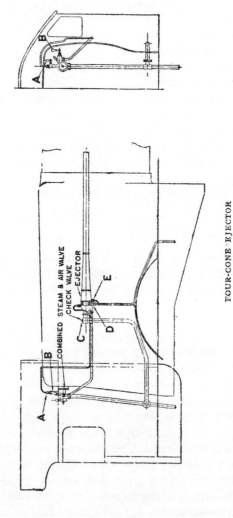

FOUR-CONE EJECTOR

Figure 11   The four-cone ejector: A—the small ejector; B—the main steamvalve; C—the ejector body; D & E—Drainage pipes. Note: A controls one cone and B the remaining three. (*C. H. Mathers, 'The Vacuum Brake' Wilding & Son Limited*)

to raise the vacuum quickly to release the brakes, and were powerful enough to keep the brakes off even when the communication cord was pulled. General fitting of the four-cone ejector began in 1913.[28]

CARRIAGES AND WAGONS

The unpopularity of the 'Dreadnought' carriages led to the construction in 1906–07 of new stock with a more conventional layout and doors to each compartment. At the same time the maximum body width was reduced to 9 feet, as the 9 feet 6 inches of the 'Dreadnoughts' was too wide for South Wales expresses. In order not to exceed the overall width, all the doors were slightly recessed, and the resulting 'in and out' appearance of the side of a coach caused this stock to be nicknamed the 'Concertinas'. As the traffic department still wanted 70 foot coaches, this length was retained. In 1907 the so-called 'Toplight' stock began to appear, in both corridor and non-corridor varieties and in various lengths up to 70 feet. Their name was derived from the hammered glass toplights above the windows. These carriages remained the standard until after Churchward's retirement.[29]

Steel underframes were general for wagon stock. The 10 ton open goods wagons and the covered ones followed closely the Railway Clearing House specifications for private owners' wagons. For conveying coal to running sheds some 20 ton all-steel wagons were built. They had the advantage that they weighed 3 tons less than the 10 ton wagons and one of them was 14 feet shorter over the buffers than two 10 ton wagons and cost 20 per cent less to build. A limited number of 40 ton capacity coal wagons with bogies were built and put into service. However, only the larger locomotive depots, which used large quantities of fuel of the same grade, really wanted wagons of that capacity. In practice, therefore, the 40-ton wagons worked mainly between South Wales collieries and the depot at Old Oak Common in London. They were not economical to build because one of them cost 28 per cent more than two 20 ton wagons and only saved 2 feet in length over the buffers. The bogie adopted for the 40 ton wagons was a modification of the diamond frame type common in American practice.[30]

NOTES

1   W. N. Pellow, letter to the author.
2   K. J. Cook, The Late G. J. Churchward's Locomotive Development on the Great Western Railway, *Journal of the Institution of Locomotive Engineers,*

Paper No. 492 (March–April 1950); H. Holcroft, *An Outline of Great Western Locomotive Practice* (London, Locomotive Publishing Co., 1957), p. 86.

3 Ibid., p. 119.

4 W. N. Pellow, letter to the author.

5 Ibid.

6 R. F. Hanks, letter to the author.

7 Holcroft, op. cit., p. 122.

8 O. S. Nock, *The GWR Stars, Castles & Kings* (Newton Abbot, David & Charles, 1967), Part 1, p. 42*f*.

9 Holcroft, op. cit., p. 125.

10 Ibid., p. 133.

11 Ibid., pp. 134–5.

12 Cook, op. cit.

13 E. T. MacDermot, *History of the Great Western Railway*, vol. II (London, Great Western Railway, 1931), p. 550.

14 W. N. Pellow, letter to the author.

15 Holcroft, op. cit., pp. 127–8, 148.

16 Cook, op. cit.

17 W. N. Pellow, letter to the author.

18 Cook, op. cit.

19 W. N. Pellow, letter to the author.

20 Holcroft, op. cit., p. 93; Sir William Stanier, 'George Jackson Churchward, Chief Mechanical Engineer Great Western Railway', *Transactions of the Newcomen Society*, **XXX** (1960).

21 Holcroft, op. cit., pp. 103*f*; Cook, op. cit.

22 O. S. Nock, *The LNWR Precursor Family* (Newton Abbot, David & Charles, 1966), p. 67.

23 Cook, op. cit.

24 H. Holcroft, *Locomotive Adventure* (London, Ian Allan), p. 59.

25 Ibid., p. 64.

26 W. N. Pellow, letter to the author; H. Holcroft, letter to the author.

27 W. N. Pellow, letter to the author.

28 C. H. Mathers, *The Vacuum Brake ... as Used on British Railways Western Region* (Shrewsbury, Wilding & Son, 3rd edn, 1948); H. Holcroft, letter to the author; R. F. Hanks. letter to the author.

29 M. Harris, *Great Western Coaches* (Newton Abbot, David & Charles, 1966), pp. 70*f*.

30 H. Holcroft, letter to the author; W. N. Pellow, letter to the author.

Chapter 12

Locomotive Exchange

'Because one of mine could pull two of their bloody things backwards!'
So said an outraged Churchward when, at a Board meeting, a Director
asked him to explain why the London & North Western Railway could
build three 4–6–0 locomotives for the same price as two of his. The
Director concerned had apparently read some articles and correspondence published in *The Engineer* in 1909, in which the Great Western
Railway was criticised on the grounds that its expenditure on locomotive
renewals and repairs was higher than that of any other railway. As a
result of this incident, it was proposed, apparently by Churchward, that
there should be an exchange between the London & North Western
Railway and the Great Western Railway of non-superheated 4–6–0
locomotives to see how they compared in service.[1]

Since this exchange took place, commentators have often referred to
the great disparity in power between Churchward's four-cylinder *Stars*
and the two-cylinder *Experiment* class of the LNWR. But this is really
being wise after the event. George Whale's 4–4–0 *Precursors* and 4–6–0
Experiments had set up standards of running with heavy trains which
gave solid backing to the London & North Western's proud claim to be
the 'Premier Line'. It was perhaps natural that Directors, without the
mechanical knowledge to appreciate the outstanding quality of Churchward's engines, should believe that the comparatively small and cheap
locomotives, which took the heavy Scotch expresses over Shap, might
do equally well with the West Country services over the formidable South
Devon banks. Further, Whale's engines had already shown up well in
comparative running against bigger engines belonging to other companies.

The *Precursor* class were turned out from Crewe from March 1904
onwards. The boiler was an enlarged version of that fitted to Webb's
famous little *Precedent* class 2–4–0s and to his *Cauliflower* (so-called
from the ornate scroll-surrounded emblem of the LNWR which adorned
the splashers) express goods 0–6–0s; whilst the cylinders and Joy valve

145

gear were similar to those of the latter class.[2] In fact the new engines embodied all that was best in the Crewe practice established by Ramsbottom and developed by Webb.

In June 1908 the *Precursors* were matched against Ivatt's 251 class large-boiler Atlantics of the Great Northern Railway. When these latter engines appeared in 1902 they were probably the most impressive looking in Great Britain, and the Great Northern made the most of them in its publicity. Churchward, as we have seen, took a great interest in their wide fireboxes. An exchange was arranged in which *Precursor* class No. 412 *Marquis* went to the Great Northern and worked trains between King's Cross and Leeds; whilst Atlantic No. 1449 hauled the London & North Western 10 a.m. Scotch express and 1.20 p.m. Irish Boat Train northward from Euston to Crewe and Stafford, respectively, returning on other heavy trains. There was not much to choose between the two types of engine either in performance or in fuel consumption, but the smaller LNWR 4-4-0 had equalled, at any rate, the big Atlantic, which was regarded by many as the outstanding British locomotive of the time.[3]

The first of the 4-6-0 *Experiment* class 4-6-0s was completed in April 1905. The cylinders and valve arrangements were the same as those of the *Precursors*, but the coupled wheels were only 6 feet 3 inches in diameter instead of 6 feet 9 inches, and there was a new boiler with a necessarily shallow firebox, which entailed a different method of firing. (The six-coupled wheels did not allow room for the deep grate of the *Precursors*.)[4] The *Experiments* soon showed a remarkable turn of speed, and Rous-Marten timed one of them at $93\frac{1}{2}$ m.p.h. between Shap Summit and Carlisle.

A month after the *Precursor* and Atlantic locomotive exchange, comparative running was arranged between *Experiment* class No. 2630 *Buffalo* and the celebrated and legendary Caledonian 4-6-0 No. 903 *Cardean* on trains between Crewe and Carlisle. *Cardean* produced the better performance, but not by much; and she was, on paper at any rate, a considerably more powerful engine, with 20 inch cylinders, as compared with *Buffalo*'s 19 inch, and a much bigger boiler with a pressure of 200 lb./in.[2] instead of *Buffalo*'s 175 lb./in[2]. The running of the London & North Western engine was, in fact, extremely good.[5]

Another comparative working involving an *Experiment* took place shortly after the interchange trials between the Great Western and the London & North Western. In October 1910 *Experiment* class No. 1483 *Redgauntlet* was matched against North British Railway Atlantic No. 881 *Borderer* between Preston and Carlisle. Again, the Atlantic was the bigger and more powerful engine. Although *Borderer* made slightly the better time up the final 4 miles at 1 in 75 to Shap Summit, it was at a cost of 71 pounds of coal per mile as compared with *Redgauntlet*'s 58 pounds. The maximum speed recorded by *Borderer* was 76 m.p.h. and by *Redgauntlet* 80 m.p.h.[6]

In the light of these results the London & North Western Railway had every reason to be satisfied with its express locomotives, and as on paper a Great Western *Star* appeared very similar in dimensions and tractive effort to *Cardean*, they may well have expected the Great Western engines to show a slight superiority, though insufficient to justify the greater capital cost.

The arrangements made between the LNWR and the GWR were that an *Experiment* class engine should run on the Great Western and a *Star* on the London & North Western for a fortnight in mid-August 1910 when both railways had to deal with the heaviest traffic of the year. The period selected was at Churchward's express wish, in order that the heavy trains could demonstrate to his Board the clear superiority of his engines.[7]

The LNWR contender on the Great Western was No. 1471 *Worcestershire* and No. 4003 *Lode Star* was selected to oppose her. No. 4005 *Polar Star* went to the London & North Western to compete with No. 1455 *Herefordshire*.

The position of the Great Western water troughs presented a difficulty to *Worcestershire*'s crew, because they were farther apart than on the London & North Western system, and the *Experiment* tenders held only 3000 gallons of water, as compared with the 3500 of the *Stars*. The Great Western did what they could to help. Arrangements were made for all troughs on the Paddington–Bristol and Paddington–Plymouth lines to be kept full, and *Worcestershire*'s water scoop was lowered an inch to ensure that the maximum amount of water could be picked up.[8]

Worcestershire was given a week of trial running so that her driver and fireman could learn the routes over which they would have to work; and then running started in earnest in accordance with the following programme:

First Day   Down 9 a.m. semi-fast Paddington–Bristol.
              Up 5.5 p.m. 2-hour express Bristol–Paddington.
Second Day Down 11 a.m. 2-hour express Paddington–Bristol.
              Up 5.54 p.m. heavy Bristol–Paddington express, with dining-car portions from Plymouth and Cardiff.

Third Day	Down 10.30 a.m. *Cornish Riviera Limited* express, Paddington–Plymouth non-stop in 4 hours 7 minutes.
Fourth Day	Up 8.30 a.m. Plymouth–Paddington express.
Fifth Day	Down 11.50 a.m. Paddington–Exeter express, non-stop in 3 hours, for Torquay.
Sixth Day	Up 12.5 p.m. Exeter-Paddington non-stop express.

Whilst *Worcestershire* was working these trains during the first week, *Lode Star* was hauling the corresponding trains in the opposite direction; e.g. on the third day, the up *Cornish Riviera* from *Plymouth*. During the second week the same trains were worked, but with *Lode Star* taking the above programme and *Worcestershire* the trains hauled by *Lode Star* in the first week.

The LNWR men on *Worcestershire* did extremely well, but it was apparent that the tasks set were beyond the capacity of their engine. *Worcestershire* was driven hard in the true LNWR tradition, but her coal consumption was enormous and time was dropped; whereas to *Lode Star* the schedules presented, of course, no problem at all.[9]

Polar Star, running on the London and North Western, had a much easier task on that railway's services, and worked them on a much smaller coal consumption than the competing *Herefordshire*. R. A. Riddles was an apprentice at Crewe when *Polar Star* arrived. He says: 'The trial with *Polar Star* took place whilst I was at Crewe, and I saw this beautiful engine come into the station—the paint immaculate, the motion beautifully machined, and the footplate fittings polished. The engine not only *was* good, it *looked* good. Bowen Cooke had to do something and designs for the *Claughton* class were worked out. But there seemed to be the same old outlook and the same old questions asked: 'What parts can we use that we have patterns for? How shall we make the boiler, using as many of the existing press blocks as possible?' The result was a lost opportunity, for the boiler was much too small and inefficient. Even when a new and bigger boiler was fitted in later years it never matched up to the job, which depended as before on the skill of the driver and the hard work of the fireman for its achievement.'[10] How different was this approach to Bowen Cooke's *Claughton* from Churchward's design of his *Stars*!

Of North Western engines in general, Riddles says:

'The frame plates were too thin in section and had to be continually welded up; strengthening plates had to be put over the horn blocks; and with the heavy and cumbersome Joy's valve gear it was impossible to get constant lead in the valve opening in all positions of the reversing gear, and fractures of the motion were frequent. It was only when initial inspection was introduced that flaws were discovered and failures prevented. But whatever the merits or demerits of the stud, they (the super-heated *George the Fifth* class) would haul 420 tons out of Euston, sparks flying to high heaven, and many times during the periods of holiday traffic I have watched trains arrive at Crewe from London and heard the shed "turner" say to the driver, "Is she all right, mate?". On getting the affirmative the tender would be coaled from a wagon alongside in Crewe station, and off she would go to Liverpool, Manchester, Holyhead, or Carlisle. The drawing office, as I knew it, "went cheap" and there was little in the way of failures to guide them. It was the good work of drivers, firemen, and shed staff, combined with North Western pride, that produced the results, despite defects in the tools they were given.'[11]

In this passage there is the whole answer to critics of Churchward's policy. There was, indeed, something magnificent about these cheap engines which, with their devoted crews, rattled and roared to reach their destinations on time, even with trains theoretically beyond their capacity. But if their initial cost was low, their fuel consumption and maintenance costs were extremely high. And even on a power-to-weight ratio the *Experiments* were no match for Churchward's *Stars*. In *The Railway and Travel Monthly* of 1911[12] there is an interesting comparison between runs behind *Worcestershire*, hauling 5·5 times her own weight, and Churchward's *Knight of the Garter* at the head of a train weighing 6·1 times her own weight. The LNWR engine, says the article, was beaten 'uphill, downhill, and on the level, 2 minutes behind at Reading, 6 minutes at Savernake, and 10 minutes at Westbury, after allowing for the water stop.'

An anonymous article in *The Railway and Travel Monthly* of 1911 by a Great Western driver shows the opinion held by the enginemen of Churchward and how, unlike Whale and Bowen Cooke, he provided them with the tools for the job. The driver writes:[13]

'I have had charge of one of Mr G. J. Churchward's four-cylinder 4–6–0 superheated engines since they were first built, and am now running one of the "Kings", which, in my humble opinion, are Kings in more senses than one. A friend of mine calls them "Kings of their race". . . .

'. . . Having set the engine in the right position, I take oil cans, feeders, hammer, set pin spanner, etc., under the engine, first trying all the set bolts in big and little ends, also making sure that all split pins, bolts and nuts, etc. are in position and properly secured. I may mention here that our chief engineer is very keen on this matter of examination, and rightly so, and although a fitter has previously been around the engine this does not in any way relieve me of my responsibilities.

'I then begin the oiling of the various parts, taking care to see that the trimmings and corks are in good working order, also a perfect fit. I am a great believer in the old-fashioned worsted trimming and caned cork for big ends, etc., no wire trimmings for me thanks, and I think our chief is of the same opinion, for he leaves it to us to trim the various parts to our liking, which I think is the proper thing to do; a driver likes to know he is trusted in matters of this kind, and lives up to the trust reposed in him.

'After very carefully oiling everything getatable from underneath, I then begin operations outside, paying careful attention to trimmings and corks as before, filling the axle boxes, etc., as full as I think will be sufficient to take me through. I should like here to pay a tribute to our chief for the splendid system of padding, etc., he has adopted with the axle boxes, for after once oiling we have no anxiety regarding them. . . .

'A good many people have asked me what it feels like when on an engine running at high speeds. Well, for one thing, our engines ride so well and steady that we scarcely realise we are travelling as fast as we are. . . .'

This article tells us more about Churchward's engines than many a technical description. It was not only the basic design that made them so good, but also a high standard of workmanship and meticulous attention to detail. They carried out their allotted tasks, including the hardest running in the country, with quiet and effortless efficiency.

The trials of 1910 did not result in any feature of Great Western design being adopted by the London & North Western; and it was not till after the visit to the West Coast route in 1926 of No. 5000 *Launceston Castle* (virtually a superheated version of *Polar Star* with a larger boiler) that the *Royal Scots*, incorporating Churchward principles, were produced to solve for a time LMS difficulties with their heaviest expresses.

On the Great Western Churchward had made his point for all to see, and there were no further suggestions that his engines were needlessly expensive.

The pure Churchward design triumphed again thirty-eight years later, when a 28xx class 2–8–0 locomotive, burning its normal diet of

Welsh coal, produced a consumption of 2·64 pounds per drawbar horse-power, which was the lowest figure for any class of engine in the entire series of tests carried out during the locomotive exchanges of 1948.[14]

NOTES

1 O. S. Nock, *The G.W.R. Stars, Castles, and Kings* (Newton Abbot, David & Charles, 1967), pp. 47*f*.
2 O. S. Nock, *The LNWR Precursor Family* (Newton Abbot, David & Charles, 1966), pp. 12*f*.
3 Ibid., pp 36–7; C. J. Allen, *The Locomotive Exchanges* (London, Ian Allan, 1950), pp. 19*f*.
4 Nock, *The Precursor Family*, pp. 40*f*.
5 Allen, op. cit.
6 Ibid.
7 Nock, *G.W.R. Stars, etc.*, pp. 47*f*.
8 Allen, op. cit., p. 30.
9 Ibid., pp. 31–3.
10 Colonel H. C. B. Rogers, *The Last Steam Locomotive Engineer: R. A. Riddles, C.B.E.* (London, George Allen & Unwin, 1970), pp. 29, 30.
11 Ibid.
12 'British Express Trains and Locomotives', *The Railway and Travel Monthly* **II**, p. 53 (January–June 1911).
13 'On the Footplate of the World's Longest Non-Stop Run', ibid., **2**, p. 117 (January–June 1911).
14 Allen, op. cit., p. xxiv.

Chapter 13

George Jackson Churchward

One of the most striking characteristics about Churchward was the devotion that he inspired in most of those who worked under him. One of them was Harry Holcroft, who, in a letter written to the author shortly before he died, said that when he was leaving the Great Western Railway in 1914 he sought a farewell interview with Churchward, who asked him what job he was going to. When Holcroft told him, he said, with a twinkle in his eye: 'Now, remember this; wherever you may go, or whatever you may do, always stick up for the Great Western.' And Holcroft, at the age of ninety-one, adds: 'This I am endeavouring to carry out.'

It is difficult, indeed, to recall any other engineer who had such a magnetic and dominating personality, that, not only were his decisions unquestioned during his tenure of office, but after his retirement and up till the time when the Great Western ceased to exist as a separate railway, no departure, save in detail, was permitted at Swindon from the standards and practices that he had established. This was the more strange, in that his immediate successor, C. B. Collett, was one of the few people who did not like him; and yet he adhered more closely than would probably have done Churchward himself to the model of the latter's standard locomotive classes. For Churchward, progressive engineer that he was, would, one feels, have taken note of advanced techniques at home and overseas to develop new standard types to meet demands for heavier and faster traffic.

Churchward's appearance inspired awe in people who never even spoke to him. R. F. Hanks remembers the tour of the Works, with Churchward leading an impressive entourage of individuals, marshalled in order of seniority.[1] Holcroft says that in bearing and mannerisms Churchward resembled the traditional country squire, with his informal tweed suits and rather slow and deliberate movements and speech. W. N. Pellow endorses this; he says: 'Churchward was a big man in every way. In physique he was large and heavy, and he had broad mental outlook. He was fond of such outdoor sports as shooting and fishing. With two or three friends he rented a considerable acreage of rough shooting on the Wiltshire Downs, and during the fishing season he would visit mid-Wales, where he rented a stretch of the River Wye for trout and salmon.'[2] Pellow adds that he enjoyed motoring in the early days, but gave it up as he grew older. For a time he used the car to visit relatives and friends in South Devon, but in later years he generally travelled there by train. Hanks says that he was unusual amongst railway officers at the time in wearing a trilby hat. Collett wore a tall bowler whilst foremen wore a normal bowler. He adds: 'In my day bowlers were a mark of authority and were to be feared!'[3]

Churchward never married. Of his brother John's marriage to his first cousin, there was born a half-wit who died of tuberculosis at the age of twenty-one. It may well be that the apparent result of his brother, the son of cousins, marrying a first cousin, deterred him from marriage. He never visited Rowes Farm after it passed into the possession of his eccentric and rather peculiar brother John. His sisters, Mary and Adelina, moved in due course to St Andrews Road in Paignton, and G. J. Churchward always stayed there when he visited South Devon.[4] It is probable that one of the large houses in this road which have now become hotels belonged to the Churchward sisters, and standing in this road one can still hear the whistle of a Great Western engine from the Torbay Steam Railway at the bottom of the hill.

In Stoke Gabriel churchyard there is a grave with a tombstone inscribed: 'In loving memory of Mary Churchward who died March 25th 1940 aged 77. Also George Jackson C.B.E. who died December 14th 1933. Also of Adelina sister of the above who died September 16th 1951 aged 85.' G. J. C. was buried at Swindon, and his inclusion here testifies to the close relationship between brother and sister. One may guess that the first two inscriptions were due to Adelina.

At some big dinner Churchward's leg was gently pulled, in an after-dinner speech, in reference to his bachelor status as compared with the happier position of his married contemporaries. In his reply, Churchward retaliated with: 'A lot of you are big men—important men; and doing big jobs, where what you say goes. But what are you when you get home? Worms! Bloody worms!'

G. J. Churchward must have kept up some contact with his cousin, Brigadier-General P. R. S. Churchward, for in 1920 the latter wrote to him about a scrape which his son, Paul Rycaut Shordiche, had got into.

Paul junior (known to his relatives and friends as 'Bob') had, in company with some other schoolboys, been attending a holiday crammer's establishment at Basildon Vicarage in Goring-on-Thames. It was close to the Paddington–Bristol main line of the Great Western Railway, and they had been caught trying to drop stones from a bridge down the chimneys of the engines which passed underneath, including the celebrated *Great Bear*. There was the threat of prosecution and the dismal prospect of the birch; but G. J. C. intervened and the prosecution was dropped. (Bob, in 1932, led an expedition to Brazil to map the mysterious Rio das Mortes and also to search for the explorer Lieutenant-Colonel Fawcett who had vanished in the area. They did not unfortunately find Fawcett, but the expedition contributed much to the knowledge of this region, and a most fascinating account of it is contained in a book written by Bob Churchward after his return.)

G. J. Churchward was not the only one of the family to be connected with railways. General Churchward's elder brother, William Patrick, had a lot to do with Italian railways and was given an honour by the Italian Government for his work. In addition his uncle, Joseph Churchward, had, with two sons, been much connected with railway affairs. In 1854 Joseph, in partnership with a Mr Jenkins, acquired the mail contract between Dover and Calais, and held it until in 1862 it was transferred to the London Chatham & Dover Railway. One son, Alaric, became LC&DR marine superintendent at Queenborough and in 1889 the railway's Paris agent; continuing in that post under the South Eastern & Chatham Railway Joint Committee. Another son, George Dundas, married Frederick Churchward's other daughter, May. He was a railway engineer and built the Tientsin-Tangshan Railway, the opening of which was celebrated with a thousand fireworks. Whether G.J.C. kept in touch with these cousins is not, unfortunately, known but one likes to think that they occasionally visited the house in St Andrews Road.

Churchward's visits to the drawing office at Swindon are vividly described by W. N. Pellow, who spent some years engaged on boiler and engine design and associated details. He saw quite a lot of Churchward, who would often come into the main office to look at something in which he was interested. On several occasions, coming to Pellow's board, he would say: 'Now then, my son, get off that stool and let me sit down; you are younger than I am. What have you got to show me today?' Then the discussion would start, and Churchward would be quick to tell Pellow in no uncertain terms whether or not he approved of the particular scheme. If he did not approve, one of the expressions he would use was: 'It's no good: that cock won't fight.' Pellow thought that Churchward must have picked this up from cockfighting in the days of his youth.

One of the tasks given to Pellow was the design of outside pipes to supply steam to the cylinders. The existing Great Western practice of having copper pipes arranged in the smokebox, just in front of the front tubeplate, was cumbersome and difficult to fit; and, in addition, it screened a lot of the boiler tubes, making it awkward for the tube cleaners and others to do their daily servicing at locomotive depots. Pellow was told to scheme out an arrangement of pipes whereby steam would flow from the regulator valve, out through the sides of the smokebox, and direct to the cylinder steam chests. The arrangement had to be such that it could be applied to as many types of locomotives as possible—to be, in fact, a standard fitting. One day, after he had been engaged on this project for some time, Pellow happened to look up and saw G. J. Churchward heading in his direction accompanied by the Chief Draughtsman, G. H. Burrows.

Arriving at Pellow's board, Churchward said: 'Well, my son, how are you getting on with this contraption?' Burrows then started to explain some of the scheme that Pellow had produced. Churchward stopped him abruptly, saying: 'Shut up, Burrows. Let the boy talk. He has done the job so far, so good, and knows what he is doing.' 'Collapse of Burrows!' comments Pellow, 'And me in fear and trembling of them both!' He adds, 'We eventually did get out an arrangement, which was later made standard for as many locomotive types as could be fitted with it.[5]

Churchward's picturesque language was proverbial; in striking contrast to that of Collett, who succeeded him. It is said that on one occasion when Churchward and Collett were inside a firebox in the boiler shop, Collett called out to a fitter: 'Pass me the illuminant' (a gas flare in those days). The fitter had no idea what an illuminant was, and hesitated. Churchward translated: 'Pass the bloody light!'[6] This was the sort of incident which would be repeated to many an appreciative audience; for his workpeople almost adored their autocratic and colourful chief. He could, indeed, give a workman a good dressing down, but it was over in a few minutes and no hard feelings remained on either side.

Churchward had an endearing delight in the mild practical joke. J. R. Rowe was told the following story by his father who was a charge-fitter. The 'B' locomotive erecting shop was in charge of a bluff but capable foreman, known as 'Buck' Bruford. One day he was visited by Churchward, who, after conversing about various jobs, departed, saying that he was going to visit Plaister, foreman of the much larger 'A' erecting shop about 300 yards away. Bruford, after being delayed on the way, returned to his office and promptly telephoned Plaister, telling him to put his boxing gloves on as the 'Old Man' was on his way. A voice at the other end thanked him for his warning. Sometime after, at a convivial gathering attended by the foremen, Churchward mentioned this incident and, amidst roars of laughter from all but Bruford, revealed that it was he who had answered the telephone and not Plaister.

Churchward was regular in his daily routine. His house, 'Newburn', was built on land adjacent to the main line and had a wicket gate in the garden fence giving access to a footpath running alongside the down main line. Each morning he would leave his house by this gate and walk along the path on his way to his office, often passing through a number of workshops, where he looked at the progress of various jobs and talked to the foreman or chargeman concerned. He would arrive in his office at about 9 a.m., depending on how long he had spent in discussions on the way. At 5 p.m. he would leave the office, to give the staff half an hour to clear up.[7] He disliked unpunctuality. One morning, approaching his office at about 9.10, he saw many female clerks still on their way to work. As soon as he entered the office he telephoned the chief clerk and asked him at what time his 'bloody hens' were supposed to start work.[8]

Churchward's attention to detail in the practical running of his engines is illustrated by the following incident. He was standing one day on a platform at Frome station, awaiting a connecting train for the Bristol branch line. When the train came in, he noticed that the fireman was standing with his head and shoulders leaning out of the cab in order to inspect the injector overflow. Churchward walked up to him and warned him that if he leaned out like that too often he could get his head knocked off. The fireman explained that it was the only way he could tell if the injector was working properly. 'But surely', said G.J.C., 'you can hear the injector sing when it is operating.' 'No', replied the fireman, 'I can't.' The great man thereupon mounted the footplate where he remained for the remainder of the journey. When the injector was put on he had to admit that he could not hear it sing. The upshot was that, within a matter of days, supplies of a modified injector overflow pipe were produced by Swindon for fitting to all engines of this type and which enabled the fireman to see the overflow without leaning out of the cab.[9]

Some mention of the estrangement between Churchward and Inglis has been made in Chapter 10. Sir Felix Pole, the famous General

Manager of the Great Western Railway, says[10] that at that time the Locomotive and Carriage Superintendent (styled Chief Mechanical Engineer from 1916) had quite an unusual status in the railway counsels. He thought that this was due partly to the prominence given to the post by Sir Daniel Gooch, and partly to Churchward's personal qualities. Churchward's standing, not only in railway circles but in the world of mechanical engineering at large, was as great as that of Inglis in civil engineering, and both, he says, were men of dominating personality. When Inglis became General Manager, he produced a chart in which the General Manager was shown as the principal executive, with consequent sole right or direct access to the Board. Besides Churchward, the Secretary, Solicitor, and Chief Accountant had hitherto had access to the Board, and all were opposed to Inglis's draft reorganisation. None of the latter three, however, had such a strong personality as Churchward, and he became the leader of the opposition to Inglis. Against such a combination Inglis made little progress.

During Inglis's tour of office from 1903 to 1911 there was a great increase of traffic, and the total receipts increased vastly in consequence. At the same time, expenses also rose, so that dividends remained the same at an average of $5\frac{1}{2}$ per cent. One result of this increase in expenditure was severe criticism by Inglis of the cost of the Locomotive and Carriage Departments;[11] and hence, of course, the comparison with the LNWR expenditure, which led to the locomotive exchange of 1910.

As regards the locomotive accounts; under the peculiar system then prevailing, the Chief Accountant, when preparing the accounts, would enquire of the Locomotive & Carriage Superintendent whether the number of locomotives that had been renewed was adequate, based on their estimated life. The latter would then agree that he should have renewed a larger number. The Accountant then charged the accounts the cost of renewing, say, 150 locomotives, whereas the actual number might be 130. The difference between the actual and theoretical expenditure was held in suspense, and appeared as a liability in the balance sheet under 'Sundry Outstanding Accounts'. Years afterwards Pole asked Churchward why he had not told Inglis that the sums appearing in the accounts were in excess of the actual expenditure on locomotive renewals. Churchward replied: 'He was mad; had I told him he would have spent the money.'[12]

Churchward did not take kindly to conditions after the First World War. During that war the Government had made large concessions to the trade unions, and at a conciliation meeting trade union representatives put forward demands which G.J.C. told them were unacceptable and impossible. They promptly retorted that under the Government concessions (which had been agreed with the unions without consultation with the railways) he could no longer reject their demands out of hand but had to negotiate a settlement. 'I can see', commented Churchward, 'that it is time the "Old Man" retired.'[13] And at the end of 1921 he did.

When the time came for Churchward's retirement, Pellow was still in the Swindon drawing office, and remembers that everyone wanted to contribute towards a retirement present—the 'rank and file', as well as the officers of the department. Subscriptions flooded in from all over the line: from Paddington to Birkenhead, Paddington to Fishguard, and Paddington to Penzance. Pellow was one of those at a packed meeting in the main hall of the Swindon Mechanics' Institute where the presentation was made. On the platform there were officers of the various sections and the Works Committee. The Chairman of the Works Committee, in a laudatory speech, expressed the staffs' appreciation of Churchward as their chief, and finished by hoping that every hair of his head would be a candle to light him to glory. Churchward, who was completely bald on top, turned round to interject: 'There won't be many of them, Watkins!' Other speeches followed, and when the time came for the 'Old Man' to reply, he was so overcome that he could hardly start. Finally, he said that he could not accept all the money, which represented so much loyalty and respect, but would like to buy a jolly good salmon and trout rod and tackle in remembrance, He would like the remainder of the money to be put into a trust fund, the interest from which should be used to provide a number of book prizes each year for the best results shown by students at the Technical School.[14]

As a result of this request, a sum of about £500 was invested and 'The Churchward Memorial Fund' established, from which many successful students have been awarded prizes. From about 1950 Pellow has been one of the three Trustees of the Fund. Owing to the changes in the railway world, the Trustees, in fairly recent times, had the Fund registered under the Charities Act 1960 and renamed 'The Churchward Trust'.[15]

Collett, when he took over as CME, did not wish to use the official residence, so Churchward continued to live at 'Newburn' and to use the path along the railway line for his morning exercise and to keep in touch with the Great Western Railway world.[16]

Not much is known of Churchward's private life. Apart from his sisters, his few intimate friends seem to have been those with whom he went shooting and fishing. These activities, together with anything mechanical, appear to have been his main interests. If he could not indulge these hobbies outside, he pursued them at home; for 'Newburn' was said to have contained a workshop, a billiard room, and a shooting gallery.[17] Always said to be closely associated with G.J.C. in his private workshop activities was a great Swindon character named Ben Hale. Latterly he was head foreman of all the Locomotive Works machine shops, including the 'O' shop, in which was the tool room. Early in his career Ben Hale went to the USA with the *Lord of the Isles* as engine erector. Rather strangely, he also wore a trilby hat.[18]

One Saturday afternoon J. R. Rowe's father was told to transport a lathe to 'Newburn', bed it down, and set it up for operation. The housekeeper answered the door and then went to fetch Churchward, who soon appeared, wearing carpet slippers and with his hands thrust deep into the front-slitted pockets of his trousers. Rowe senior explained his mission, upon which Churchward took him into the workshop and showed him what he wanted done. 'When you have completed it call me', he said. When in due course the job was finished, Churchward gave it a critical inspection, and then thanked Rowe and gave him a golden sovereign. He then took Rowe aside and asked him: 'Who is that chap with you?' Rowe said that he was his younger brother, who had given him a hand with the lifting. 'That's all right Rowe,' said Churchward, 'in that case you had better put this into his hand', giving him a half-sovereign.[19]

Churchward retained to the end of his life a lively interest in what went on in the railway world, and when he had an opportunity to talk to anyone of his old department, he would put questions on all sorts of matters to find out how things were going on. The last of such conversations of which there is any record was with W. N. Pellow, a few months before Churchward's death. It took place in March or April 1933 when Pellow was Divisional Locomotive Superintendent at Bristol. He got a message from Swindon that Churchward proposed to travel to Devon the following day. The service he had chosen entailed changing trains at Temple Meads station, Bristol, and Pellow was requested to meet the train from Swindon and see him safely aboard the connecting service to Newton Abbot.

Pellow arranged with his friends of the traffic department for a compartment to be reserved on the train for Newton Abbot, and was on the platform when the train came in from Swindon. As it drew to a standstill, Churchward's arm shot out towards Pellow. 'I know you', he said: 'I remember you from the drawing office days. How are you getting on?' 'He was obviously pleased to see me,' says Pellow, 'and as we had thirty minutes to wait I asked him if he would like to walk as far as the sheds. "No," he said; "let's find a seat where we can sit and chat." We did so, and he fired off question after question; asking how various types of locomotives were behaving, and what we were doing about this and that problem. Amongst other comments, he said: "There is something the matter with the 49s; their lubrication isn't right."' Churchward was referring to the *Hall*, or 49XX class, 4–6–0s, which were Collett's version of the *Saints*, with 6 foot instead of 6 foot $8\frac{1}{2}$ inch coupled wheels. Pellow explains that for years it had been the practice to fit two rings on each piston head, each ring being a little over $\frac{1}{2}$ inch wide. Churchward tried out the wear of narrow rings, and experimented for some time, watching the wear on such rings, before finally settling on a ring $\frac{1}{4}$ inch wide. Collett continued this practice, and the *Halls*, when they came out in 1928, were all fitted with pistons having narrow rings. For some reason these engines wore down their rings in service faster than most other classes. The drawing office experimental gang were turned on to the problem, and Pellow assumes that G.J.C. got to hear of it somehow and was trying to find out what was going on. Pellow was not able to help much as he had been out in the various Divisions of the Railway since 1922 and had largely lost touch with what the drawing office was doing. He knew, however, that there were two or three theories at the time. One was that the wear was due to the qualities of the oil used as a lubricant, which was possibly being adversely affected by the superheat. Another was that the quality of the metal in either the cylinders or the piston rings themselves was at fault. And a third was that there might be a particular 'hot spot' along the cylinder barrel which, so to speak, 'burnt off' the oil before it could take effect. Pellow never found out what was really wrong. As far as he knew, no similar trouble over excessive wear was ever experienced in the cylinders or rings of the *Saint*, or 29XX class, engines. Pellow told Churchward about these various theories and remembers him saying: 'If I was there now, I would take some sample borings from a few cylinder castings of the 49s and also from the cylinders of the 29s and make comparisons, as I would not put it past those rascals in the Iron Foundry to have been a bit free and easy sometimes when making the mixture of our cast iron for engine cylinder blocks.' Pellow comments: 'I thought at the time that the "Old Man" was wise to what could go on in the Works. He could easily have got his "Lab" to analyse a number of sample borings and so check up on the quality of the cast iron.'

'The time,' says Pellow, 'fled by. The train by which he was to travel ran in, and I picked up his overcoat to escort him to his compartment. "Hey!" he yelled, "Go easy with that coat; my flask and sandwiches are in the pockets." Just typical of him! When I put him on the train he badly wanted me to travel on with him: "Just as far as Taunton, say. I wish you would; we have had an enjoyable yarn." Unfortunately I had a special meeting to attend in Bristol and it could not be managed. That was the last chance I had to talk with the grand old man.'[20]

This conversation with Pellow perhaps brings out more of Churchward's true character than any other recorded incident. It shows, too, his continued enthusiasm, up to the end of his life, in things mechanical and in steam locomotives particularly. One senses, too, a possible feeling of frustration and a deep longing to be still in control of affairs at Swindon.

(As regards the cylinder wear on the *Halls*, K. J. Cook writes: 'There was a great deal of investigation into this as soon as it became apparent, particularly from the point of view of design, and most possibilities were discarded, except the direct steam admission by the outside steam pipes. It was difficult to appreciate why this should be, but it did appear to have an effect. Very few—none in the early days—29xx had that type of cylinder, and, of course, for the same road speed, the piston speed in the *Halls* would be higher. There was no significant difference in the cast iron.'[21])

On Tuesday 19 December 1933, at about 10 a.m. Churchward was knocked over and killed by the engine of an express train. It was a dreary morning with sufficient low-lying fog to make visibility poor. As Churchward opened the gate leading to his favourite walk along the railway line, the old man who looked after the garden at Newburn tried to persuade him not to go on account of the horrible weather. Churchward who was in his usual form, pooh-poohed the suggestion, saying that he was interested in the condition of the track, which was becoming due for relaying, particularly the sleepers. A little later, No. 4085 *Berkeley Castle* ran through Swindon on the down Fishguard express. Churchward had been getting rather deaf, and it was assumed that he was bending down looking at the track and did not hear it coming. The outer edge of the front buffer beam of the engine struck his head, killing him instantly. His body was spotted lying beside the line by the driver of an up train, which passed a few minutes later. Soon afterwards the chargeman of a plate-laying gang came across the body. K. J. Cook, then Assistant Works Manager, was in the A.E. Erecting shop in connection with the Zeiss optical equipment, when the chief foreman, Plaister, called him urgently, saying, 'The "Old Man" has been knocked down on the main line.' Cook immediately went to the spot, where he found F. A. Drinkwater, chargeman of the weigh-table and a prominent St John's First Aid man. After sending the body to the hospital, Cook telephoned from the weigh-table to R. A. G. Hannington, the Works Manager, who was completely stunned by the news. Cook then went to 'Newburn' to tell them what had happened, and whilst he was in the house Collett, who had been telephoned by Hannington, arrived.[22]

Pellow, as Divisional Locomotive Superintendent at Bristol with an area extending eastward as far as Didcot, had the melancholy duty of attending the inquest. Cook also, of course, was there, as were the driver and fireman of the engine which struck him down. The inquest was held by Dr Forrester, with a jury who were quite satisfied that it was an accident. It had been Churchward's wish that he should be buried in the Parish churchyard at Swindon, and there was a very large attendance at the funeral.[23]

On 31 January 1957 the centenary of G. J. Churchward's birth was commemorated by the Western Region of British Railways by the laying of a wreath on his grave at Christ Church, Swindon. The wreath included the outline of an engine and the initials G.J.C., and it was laid on the grave by Mr C. L. Gidsell, a sixty-eight-year-old fitter in the Erecting Shop of the Swindon Locomotive Works, who was an apprentice in Churchward's time and who was personally known to him.[24] It was an effective symbol of the tribute paid by all members of the old Railway Locomotive Department to a very great man.

R. A. G. Hannington, who was devoted to Churchward, came to a tragic end himself, for, during a visit to his daughter's school, he dived by mistake into the shallow end of the school swimming pool. His first cousin once removed, Grace, is now Bob Churchward's wife.

It would be appropriate to finish this chapter with a story from a branch of the Churchward family in the United States, and which prefigured in an extraordinary way G. J. Churchward's own death. Isaac Tappan, father-in-law of Moses Churchward, lived as an old man at Dodge Center and loved to walk into the town along the railway track. He had become deaf with age and in 1869 he was knocked down and killed by a train just east of the later Great Western Depot.[25]

NOTES

1   R. F. Hanks, letter to the author.
2   W. N. Pellow, letter to the author.
3   R. F. Hanks, letter to the author.
4   E. Hannaford Hill, information to the author; F. Robinson, information to the author.
5   W. N. Pellow, letter to the author.
6   R. F. Hanks, letter to the author; K. J. Cook, letter to the author.
7   K. J. Cook, letter to the author.
8   J. R. Rowe, communicated to the author by Miss V. M. Brown.
9   R. F. Hanks, letter to the author.
10   Felix J. C. Pole, *His Book* (Town and Country Press, Bracknell, 1968), p. 14.
11   Ibid., p. 42.
12   Ibid., p. 44.
13   H. Holcroft, letter to the author.
14   W. N. Pellow, letter to the author; Sir William Stanier, 'George Jackson Churchward, Chief Mechanical Engineer, Great Western Railway', *Transactions of the Newcomen Society*, **XXX** (1960).
15   W. N. Pellow, letter to the author.
16   Ibid.
17   J. R. Rowe, communicated to the author by Miss V. M. Brown.
18   R. F. Hanks, letter to the author.
19   J. R. Rowe, communicated to the author by Miss V. M. Brown.
20   W. N. Pellow, letter to the author.
21   K. J. Cook, letter to the author.
22   Ibid.; W. N. Pellow, letter to the author; *Great Western Railway Magazine*, **XLVI** (January 1934).
23   Ibid.
24   British Railways, Western Region, Information to the Press No. 1578.
25   Brian G. Churchward, information to the author on the Minneapolis Churchwards.

Chapter 14

The Post-Churchward Era

Before dealing with the locomotive policy that was pursued after Churchward's retirement, it is perhaps worth recapitulating the standards he had established. Many regarded the boiler as his greatest achievement. The first one that he designed, it will be recollected, was that which became his Standard No. 2. It was evolved from a comparatively large boiler with a straight-sided Belpaire firebox which was fitted to the *Duke* class 4–4–0 *Bulldog* of 1898. Subsequently a similar boiler, but without a dome was built for the *Badminton* class 4–4–0 engine *Waterford*. *Camel*, another *Duke* class engine, followed in 1899 with a boiler similar to that of *Waterford*, but with a cylindrical smokebox carried on a saddle. In 1900 *Atbara*, a modified *Badminton*, was given the same boiler as *Camel*. In 1902 the 4–6–0 *William Dean* was built with a larger boiler of the same type, and this was the precursor of Churchward's Standard No. 1.

These excellent new boilers, which would have satisfied most locomotive engineers of the time, did not, however, quite match up to Churchward's expectations. The minor troubles experienced with *William Dean's* boiler led to the design of the Standard No. 4, rather bigger than the No. 2, with a coned barrel and curved firebox side plates. This was fitted to the *Atbara* class engine *Mauritius* and was so successful that it became the model for all future standard boilers, the Nos 1 and 2 being altered to conform with it.

The Standard No. 1 boiler was common to all 4–6–0 engines during the Churchward regime, and also to the small-wheeled 2–8–0s of the 28xx class. The *Atbara, Flower, Bulldog,* and *Bird* class 4–4–0s had the No. 2 boiler, as did also the *County* tanks and the first fifty of the larger 2–6–2 tank engines. The No. 4 boiler was first fitted to the *Cities* and then to the *Counties*. The *Aberdares*, which had started with the No. 2, eventually all got the No. 4 boiler. The 2–6–2 tanks from No. 3150 onwards, the 43xx 2–6–0 tender engines, and the 2–8–0 tank engines, all had the No. 4. A small Standard No. 5 boiler was produced for the smaller 2–6–2 tank engines and for the solitary light 4–4–2 tank engine No. 4600.

The Great Bear, of course, had the much larger Standard No. 6 boiler, and the large-wheeled 47XX class 2–8–0 engines had the No. 7, which was shorter than the No. 6 but had a barrel of the same diameter.

The eventual list of standard boilers and the locomotive classes to which they were fitted as was follows:

NO.	BARREL DIAMETER	PRESSURE, lb./in.²	GRATE AREA, ft.²	CLASSES
I	4′ 10$\frac{3}{16}$″ to 5′ 6″	225	22·07	*Star* (40XX) *Saint* (29XX) 2–8–0 (28XX)
2	4′ 5$\frac{1}{8}$″ to 5′ 0$\frac{1}{2}$″	200	20·35	*Atbara/Flower* (41XX) *Bulldog/Bird* (33XX) *County Tank* (22XX) 2–6–2T (3100)
4	4′ 10$\frac{3}{4}$″ to 5′ 6″	200	20·56	*County* (38XX) *City* (37XX) 2–6–2T (3150) *Aberdare* (26XX) 2–6–0 (43XX) 2–8–0 T (42XX)
5	4′ 2″ to 4′ 9$\frac{1}{2}$″	200	16·6	2–6–2T (44XX) 2–6–2T (45XX) 4–4–2T (4600)
6	5′ 6″ to 6′ 0″	225	41	*The Great Bear*
7	5′ 6″ to 6′ 0″	225	30·28	2–8–0 (47XX)

There was also a No. 3 Standard boiler which was similar to the No. 2, but 9 inches shorter in the barrel, which was used on the 36XX class 2–4–2 suburban tank engines.

The next most important Churchward feature—and in the opinion of some, indeed, an even greater contribution to locomotive design than his boilers—was the long travel valve, combined with piston valves of large diameter and wide port openings, In fact, all other locomotive engineers, though they may not have paid much attention to Swindon boilers, were eventually compelled to follow Churchward in front end design.

The third principal feature of Churchward's locomotive practice was the large number of standard parts which were common to as many locomotives as possible. Boilers have already been discussed. Of the many other standard components, the ones which particularly strike the observer were cylinders and wheels. Most engines had two outside cylinders and they were generally of $18\frac{1}{2}$ inch diameter and 30 inch stroke. Those of the *Counties*, *County Tanks*, and 3100 2–6–2 tanks were half an inch smaller in diameter, and those of the 47xx 2–8–0s and 2–8–0 tanks were half an inch bigger. Express locomotives all had coupled wheels of 6 feet $8\frac{1}{2}$ inches in diameter; those of the mixed traffic engines (43xx, 47xx, 3100, and 3150) were 5 feet 8 inches; and the goods engines (28xx and 42xx) wheels were 4 feet $7\frac{1}{2}$ inches.

This then was the locomotive fleet that Churchward handed over to his successor; but it must be remembered that there were still large numbers of the smaller Dean and Armstrong locomotives, and these would probably need replacement before too long.

As to why C. B. Collett became CME is something of a mystery. He had had no locomotive training before coming to Swindon[1] and there was a mutual dislike between him and Churchward. He was, however, a strong personality and extremely able, and it is probable that at that time the Directors considered that, of the engineers available with the requisite seniority, Collett had the best qualifications. But he was a difficult person to serve under and was not, on the whole, popular with his subordinates.

As already noted, the last batch of *Stars*, the *Abbeys*, came out in 1922 and 1923, after Churchward had retired. Other engines of which construction was continuing were the 2–6–0 and 2–8–0 tender engines and the 2–8–0 tank engines. The *Stars* whilst still able to handle the fastest and heaviest trains, had little reserve in hand on the more arduous of the new workings. The first need which Collett had to meet, therefore, was for a more powerful express passenger engine. It was to meet such a need, of course, that Churchward had built his prototype Pacific *The Great Bear*, and discussions with the Civil Engineer's department would have shown that the major routes could soon be made to accommodate an engine of this weight and size. As an interim measure, immediately after the First World War, Churchward had wanted to fit the No. 7 boiler to the *Stars* and *Saints* to give them that extra steaming capacity to work the heaviest trains.[2] However, this would have brought the axle load above the $19\frac{1}{2}$ tons which was still the limit; and though those routes over which the *Kings* were later to work would soon be ready for a heavier weight, it was not practicable at the time to restrict any large proportion of the *Stars* and *Saints* to running over them.

Collett's solution was to build a *Star* with a boiler which was smaller than the No. 7 but bigger than the No. 1, thereby keeping the axle weight within the permitted limit, and with a larger cylinder diameter, which could be obtained by departing from Churchward's minimum tyre width of $5\frac{3}{4}$ inches. Though the new engines, the *Castle* class, were thus the result of a compromise, they were extremely successful, and the best British express passenger engines of their day. I remember seeing the first of the series, *Caerphilly Castle*, at Wembley in 1924, standing beside the much bigger LNER Pacific, *Flying Scotsman*. I was rather astonished at the notice proclaiming the former to be the most powerful passenger engine in Great Britain, but, having been brought up as a Cornishman to believe that everything the Great Western did was a bit better than the corresponding effort by any other railway, I never doubted its truth. The subsequent comparative running between the *Castles* and Gresley's Pacifics, and the triumph of the former, has been told many times, and it is not really part of the Churchward story; though it did lead to Gresley adopting Churchward's long travel valves. However, there is a passage in Sir Nigel Gresley's report to his Locomotive Committee which gives support to Churchward's belief in a Pacific with a big boiler. Gresley said that although the tractive effort of the *Castle* was higher than that of his Pacific (and also incidentally than that of *The Great Bear*) the boiler power was considerably less. So that, whilst the *Castle* could run fast on short rising grades, such as King's Cross to Finsbury Park, the Pacific ran faster on the long hill grades of the Great Western.[3]

Sir Felix Pole says[4] that one of the Directors, Sir Aubrey Brocklebank, had a considerable knowledge of locomotive practice, and in various conversations with Pole he had suggested that the *Castles* were not entirely satisfactory. Pole forgot his point of criticism, but it was probably that on certain heavy West of England and Birmingham expresses the *Castles* had very little reserve. Subsequently Pole and Brocklebank discussed the question of axle loading with Collett, who then expressed his wish for an axle load of $22\frac{1}{2}$ tons. Brocklebank, in a later conversation with Pole, said: 'I wonder what is the real carrying capacity of the main line. Obviously, the rails, if adequately supported, could carry almost any weight. The real difficulty must be the bridges. Could we not have a diagram prepared to show the maximum axle load for each bridge?' Pole said that that should be easy and asked Lloyd, the Chief Civil Engineer, to join them. And so the whole story came out as related in Chapter 10.

Collett's *King* class 4–6–0 was the really big *Star* which logically the *Castle* should have been, and it was fitted with a lengthened No. 7

boiler, known as the Standard No. 12. It is perhaps of some interest to compare the principal dimensions of the five large boilers:

Standard No.	1	6	7	8	12
Barrel length	14' 10"	23'	14' 10"	14' 10"	16'
Max diameter	5' 6"	6' 0"	6' 0"	5' 9"	6' 0"
Min diameter	4' $10\frac{13}{16}$"	5' 6"	5' 6"	5' $1\frac{15}{16}$"	5' $6\frac{1}{2}$"
Grate area, ft^2	27·7	41	30·28	30·28	34·3

The *Kings* were excellent engines, but the *Star* design was already twenty years old and the long lead that Churchward had established over other railways was being rapidly lost. There was still no advance in the degree of superheat, and yet only two years later André Chapelon was able to show that oils were available that would stand up to a very high superheat indeed, and his famous Pacific, No. 3566, of the Paris–Orleans Railway was probably as far in advance of Collett's *Kings* as Churchward's *Stars* had been ahead of any other express engines in Great Britain.

In one notable respect the *King* class departed from a Churchward standard, in that the coupled wheels were reduced from the normal express passenger size of 6 feet $8\frac{1}{2}$ inches to 6 feet 6 inches. This was, of course, an extremely expensive alteration, particularly as the bogie wheels had consequently to be reduced from the standard 3 feet 2 inches to 3 feet, because the smaller coupled wheels lowered the clearance under the inside cylinders. It has been suggested that the reason for the reduction in diameter was so that the nominal tractive effort should exceed 40 000 pounds, thus enabling a claim that the new engines were the most powerful in Great Britain to be beyond dispute. This may well be so; but it is of course conceivable tht Collett really did want to try a smaller wheel.

The cylinder dimensions of the original *Stars* had been $14\frac{1}{2}$ inches by 26 inches, whilst *The Great Bear* had cylinders of 15 inches by 26 inches. Starting with the *Prince* series, the later *Stars* had cylinders the same size as those of *The Great Bear*, because it was found that the superheated boilers could provide sufficient steam to feed these larger cylinders; and the earlier *Stars*, in due course, had their cylinders bored out to 15 inches. The cylinders of the *Castles* were increased in size to 16 inches by 26 inches, and those of the *Kings* had the maximum diameter that could be squeezed in of $16\frac{1}{4}$ inches, whilst the stroke was lengthened to 28 inches.

Collett had the weight distribution of some of the 43XX class 2–6–0 engines modified, so that there was considerably greater weight on the leading coupled axle, and some increase in weight of the engine as a whole. These modified engines were numbered in the 83xx series. Part of the reason for this modification, in Pellow's opinion, was that there had been some derailments of the pony truck wheels of the 43xx class at various places on the system, when the engines were negotiating curves of a certain radius. But these derailments might have been due in some cases to excessive speed round such curves. Collett evidently thought it desirable to increase the weight at the front end of these engines. Their adhesion was improved, but, as compared with the original design, they had the disadvantage that the heavier loading of the leading axle lifted them from the 'Blue' category into the 'Red'.[5]

(Many years previously, as a result of a survey carried out by the Civil Engineers, all Great Western lines had been classified as 'Red', 'Blue', 'Yellow', and 'Uncoloured'—code designations to show the greatest axle weights permitted to run on them. The strongest routes were the 'Red' ones, which could take engines with an axle weight up to $19\frac{1}{2}$ tons. The 'Blue' routes could take up to 17 tons 12 hundredweights; whilst the 'Yellow' were limited to 16 tons and the 'Uncoloured' to 14 tons. All locomotives bore coloured discs on their cab sides denoting the lowest category routes over which they were allowed to run. For instance, all the express passenger engines and the 47xx class were 'Red'; the *Bulldogs*, the 43xx, and the 28xx were 'Blue'; the *Dukes* and the 45xx 2–6–2 tanks were 'Yellow'; whilst Dean's 2301 class 0–6–0s were 'Uncoloured'. Routes strong enough to carry the *Kings* were 'Hatched Red', and these engines carried two red discs on their cab sides.)

Some time before Churchward's retirement, locomotive inspectors had asked for a mixed traffic engine bigger than the 43xx class, and having a bogie and a No. 1 boiler instead of the No. 4. In view of his provision of the big 47xx mixed traffic engines, Churchward did not think this request justified. Now, it will be remembered from Chapter 11 that in 1913 it was decided that all future express engines should have four cylinders and that, as a result, further construction of *Saints* was stopped. However, the *Saints* were performing excellent work on those main line services with fairly frequent stops which did not justify the use of four-cylinder engines. Collett thought they would be still more useful with a bit more tractive effort, and in 1925, as an experiment, he reduced the driving wheels of No. 2925 *Saint Martin* from a diameter of 6 feet $8\frac{1}{2}$ inches to 6 feet. The experiment was so successful that over 300 more *Saints* with 6-foot coupled wheels were built from 1928 onwards.

They were given the new class name of *Hall* and numbered in the 49xx series. *Saint Martin* was renumbered 4900 and was followed by No. 4901 *Adderley Hall*. They gradually replaced all the surviving 4–4–0 engines and were also very nearly the type of engine which the locomotive inspectors wanted.[6]

In 1936 the locomotive inspectors' suggestions were more precisely met, because Collett rebuilt eighty of the 43xx 2–6–0s as 4–6–0s, with the same 5 foot 8 inch coupled wheels and a No. 1 boiler. These became the *Grange* or 68xx class, and so, three years after his death, there appeared the type of mixed traffic engine that Churchward had envisaged in 1901.[7]

In 1938 the first of a new series of light 4–6–0s, the *Manor* or 78xx class, was turned out from Swindon. The *Granges* were 'Red' route engines, and the *Manors* were intended to provide a replacement for the 2–6–0s on the 'Blue' routes. For these engines there was designed a new No. 14 boiler with a barrel diameter of 4 ft. $7\frac{1}{8}$ inches to 5 feet 3 inches and a grate area of 22·1 ft.[2] Only twenty of these engines were built; but it is difficult to understand why any were built at all, for the boiler and cylinders were rather smaller than those of the 2–6–0s and they had less superheat. It would be interesting to know the reasons which Collett submitted to the Board for their construction.

It was C. B. Collett's practice, each year, when preparing his recommendations for the building of any new locomotives, carriages or wagons, to get the views of his principal assistants before submitting his programme to the General Manager and the Board. This was done at a meeting in his office attended by the Locomotive Works Manager, the Carriage & Wagon Works Manager, and the Locomotive Running Superintendent & Outdoor Assistant. The last of these three had to keep in touch at all times with the Traffic Superintendent in connection with the allocation of engine power to meet the requirements of both passenger and goods working; and he was responsible for submitting to the CME an assessment of new locomotives required and a list of the older types that he considered could be scrapped.

At the 1930 meeting in Collett's office, Pellow, the Assistant Locomotive Running Superintendent, had to attend because Charles Crump, the Locomotive Running Superintendent, was sick. The Locomotive Works Manager suggested that a new batch of *King* class engines should be ordered. (Twenty of these had already been built and ten more were then under construction.) Pellow said that the suggestion from the Running Department was that another batch of *Castle* class engines should be ordered. Collett immediately interjected: 'Oh! Why not more of my *King* class?' Pellow replied that if he would only refer to the route map he would know the answer to that question. He would at once see that the mileage of the routes over which the *Kings* were permitted was very limited, and the Running Superintendent already had enough *King* class engines to cover the services on such routes. Any more *Kings* would not be economical until more route miles were made available to them. Collett was not pleased with this, but finally agreed to order more engines of the *Castle* class. The next item on the agenda was the building of some more 2–6–0 engines, and Collett said he thought another lot of the 8300 series should be ordered. Pellow replied that the same argument over route availability applied in this case, as the 8300 class were in the 'Red' category and the Running Department had some difficulty in finding suitable services for the existing 'Red' engines. He suggested that some more 43xx type 'Blue' group engines should be ordered, as they were much more flexible in use. Collett was again somewhat annoyed, but he could not refute the argument and agreed to Pellow's suggestion. As a consequence of this meeting, then, no *King* class and no 8300 class engines were ordered in the building programme for the next twelve months.

When Crump returned to duty, and had a chance to speak with the other Assistants to the CME, he told Pellow that all those present at the meeting were quite expecting Collett to explode and deal severely with Pellow and were very surprised that he took the matter so quietly. However, no more *Kings* or 8300s were ever built, and the construction of the *Castle* class was resumed in the 1932 programme.[8]

It is not proposed to deal in detail with the post-Churchward locomotives on the Great Western; sufficient has been written to show how Churchward's policy was continued by his successor, though without any notable advance. The régime of F. W. Hawksworth, who succeeded Collett, was even less prolific, but Hawksworth was hampered through much of his period in office by the restrictions of the Second World War. His *County*, or 1000, class 4–6–0s were a notable departure from Churchward practice, because the boiler (styled No. 15) was copied from Stanier's LMS 2–8–0 heavy freight locomotives. These engines were adopted by the Ministry of Supply in the Second World War, and eighty of them were built at Swindon. Of course, Stanier's designs were developed from those of Churchward and the *County* was thus readily recognisable as a Great Western engine. Nevertheless, the class met no particular need and the thirty locomotives in it cannot be said to have been a real success.[9]

As one would expect, one change after Churchward's retirement was that the Chief Mechanical Engineer no longer had direct access to the Board, but came under the General Manager. The immediate visible result of this change was that the old chocolate and cream livery returned to the Great Western's coaches, and the express locomotives, after their wartime austerity dress, re-appeared in the glory of copper-capped chimneys and brass-beaded splashers; for Sir Felix Pole had an appreciation of Great Western tradition and its publicity value. R. F. Hanks, when he was Chairman of the Western Area Board, British Transport Commission (which embraced the Western Region of British Railways) agreed with and followed Pole in this respect. With the enthusiastic co-operation of K. W. C. Grand (the last General Manager of the Great Western in the old tradition), he used his influence in a number of ways to perpetuate the memory of the old Company. These included the painting of coaches composing named trains of Western Region in chocolate and cream, the move of the celebrated *City of Truro* to Swindon (from whence she worked certain special trains), the preservation of 4–6–0 No. 6000 *King George V*, and the naming of class 47 diesel locomotives after George Jackson Churchward, Isambard Kingdom Brunel, and Sir Daniel Gooch. Great Western tradition, however, was not confined to the outward appearance of locomotives and coaching stock. Hanks mentions, as a continuing Churchward tradition, the excellent footplate discipline, which was manifested by the perfect running of the engines and the punctilious observance of regulations.[10]

This chapter has been concerned with the post-Churchward era; but perhaps on the locomotive side there was no such thing. The great engineer had so stamped his personality on men and things that the Great Western remained 'Churchward' until the end of its time—and after.

NOTES

1   W. N. Pellow, letter to the author.
2   O. S. Nock, *The G.W.R. Stars, Castles, and Kings* (Newton Abbott, David & Charles, 1967), p. 89.
3   *Locomotives of the LNER Part 2A Tender Engines—Classes A1 to A10* (The Railway Correspondence & Travel Society, 1973), p. 14.
4   Felix J. C. Pole, *His Book* (Town and Country Press, Bracknell, 1968), p. 87.

5 W. N. Pellow, letter to the author.
6 K. J. Cook, 'The Late G. J. Churchward's Locomotive Development on Great Western Railway', *Journal of the Institution of Locomotive Engineers*, Paper No. 491 (March–April 1950).
7 Cook, op. cit.
8 W. N. Pellow, letter to the author.
9 K. J. Cook, information to the author.
10 R. F. Hanks, letter to the author.

Chapter 15

Churchward's Missionaries

The outstanding performances of Churchward's locomotives had so established his reputation that on certain other railways there was a growing impression that if they wanted a good locomotive man they should go to Swindon for him. This gave considerable satisfaction to Churchward, for this was the status he had sought for Swindon from the day that he took office.[1]

Rather surprisingly, perhaps, the first railway to experience the Swindon influence was the Great Southern & Western, in Ireland, and the second was the South Eastern & Chatham. But the instrument through which this influence reached both railways was R. E. L. Maunsell.

Maunsell served his apprenticeship on the Great Southern & Western Railway at its Inchicore Works under H. A. Ivatt, the then Locomotive Superintendent, who later went to the Great Northern Railway and achieved fame with his Atlantics. (The wide fireboxes of these Atlantics had, as we have noted, been admired by Churchward.) After completing his apprenticeship, Maunsell went to the Lancashire & Yorkshire Railway and worked at Horwich under J. A. F. Aspinall, who had preceded Ivatt as Locomotive Superintendent of the GS&WR. Maunsell started in the Horwich drawing office and later became Locomotive Foreman in the Blackpool District. In 1894 he went to India as Assistant Locomotive Superintendent of the East Indian Railway. In 1896 he returned to Inchicore as Works Manager. Ivatt, who was a great friend of Aspinall, had left Inchicore for Doncaster the previous year and had been succeeded by Robert Coey. It was probably Ivatt who suggested Maunsell as Works Manager. Maunsell held this appointment for fifteen years, and when Coey retired in 1911 he succeeded him as Locomotive Superintendent.[2]

Maunsell's promotion meant that a new Works Manager was required at Inchicore. The successful running of the Great Western *Stars* against the London & North Western *Experiments* had recently electrified the railway world. Maunsell had no doubt followed these trials with keen interest, and it was probably at his suggestion that approach was made to Swindon; with the result that Churchward recommended E. A. Watson for the appointment. Watson had begun his railway work at the American Locomotive Company's Shenectady Works, and from there he had gone to the Works of the Pennsylvania Railroad at Altoona. After some time with the Pennsylvania, he returned to England and became an Inspector on the Great Western Railway at Swindon. As Churchward took a great interest in American practice, Watson's experience was of value at Swindon; and his ability was recognised by his appointment as an assistant to the Locomotive Works Manager. It was at that time the practice at Swindon to give promising young men opportunities to gain experience by making them in turn assistants to the Managers of the Locomotive and the Carriage Works and to the Locomotive Running Superintendent. They were then encouraged to take up more senior appointments when these were offered on other railways, so that vacancies would be made on the Swindon 'promotion ladder'. It was intended that these young men should have a period of from three to four years in each Swindon appointment before making another move.

At Inchicore, Watson was, of course, a strong protagonist of Swindon practices, including those that had been derived from North America. But Maunsell, however much he may have wanted a Swindon man, did not apparently realise how much of the success of Great Western locomotives was due to their long travel and long lap valves, and was not convinced that all of Churchward's views were necessarily correct.[3] In this opinion he was supported by E. E. Joynt, the Chief Draughtsman at Inchicore, who had joined the GS&WR in 1892 and had been in the drawing office ever since he had finished his time as an apprentice.

In 1913 Maunsell was offered and accepted the appointment of Chief Mechanical Engineer of the South Eastern & Chatham Railway at Ashford, whilst Watson succeeded him as CME of the Great Southern & Western. Because a Swindon-inspired engine appeared first on the GS&WR, the events on that railway after Watson assumed office will be considered first.

Soon after his appointment Watson obtained from Swindon a full set of drawings of the four-cylinder *Star* class 4–6–0.[4] (This, incidentally, shows the favours extended to Swindon men; for when, after *Launceston Castle*'s impressive performance on the LMS in 1926, Sir Henry

Fowler asked Swindon for a set of *Castle* drawings, the request was refused.[5]) In 1914 Watson obtained authority from his Board to build a four-cylinder 4–6–0 express passenger locomotive. Had Watson stuck to the Swindon drawings, he would, of course, have produced a very good engine. But there were certain difficulties. The greatest of these was probably the personality of Joynt, his Chief Draughtsman, who disliked both Watson and his projected locomotive. A second difficulty was probably that it would be both unpopular and a long process to discard too many of Inchicore's traditional practices. The permitted axle weight may well have presented a third difficulty.

The First World War held up production, and it was not till 1916 that No. 400 was turned out from Inchicore Works. The engine followed Swindon practice as regards the cylinder layout and divided drive, though the Walschaerts valve gear was outside. The boiler, however, was very different with a pressure of only 175 lb./in.[2] and a high superheat. The firebox was of the Belpaire pattern, but the barrel, probably in deference to Inchicore practice, was parallel and fitted with a dome. Top feed was included, though the feed pipes were placed inside the boiler.[7] The valve travel in full gear was $5\frac{1}{4}$ inches, as compared with the $6\frac{7}{8}$ inches of the *Stars*. If the steam circuit had followed Churchward principles, No. 400 would have been satisfactory; but, as Holcroft rather nicely puts it,[8] 'Inchicore drawing office failed to appreciate certain points in Churchward's design and the results of the engine in service was disappointing.' In 1918 application was made to the Board of Trade for the release of materials for building three more engines at Inchicore; and in the following years six were ordered from Armstrong Whitworth, of which three were to use saturated steam from boilers pressed up to 225 lb/in[2]. Joynt left the service of the GS&WR in 1919 and, whilst these new engines were being delivered, Watson left too, to become General Manager of Messrs Beyer Peacock at Manchester. Watson was relieved by J. R. Bazin.[9] In 1923 Bazin got authority to fit the saturated steam engines with superheaters, because they were burning 26 per cent more coal than the others. Later he sent a set of drawings of the 400 class to Maunsell, seeking his advice on what improvements could be made to them. The drawings were passed to Holcroft to examine, but he found that short of extensive rebuilding there was little that could be done.[10] Ultimately seven of the ten engines were rebuilt with two cylinders and the other three were scrapped. The rebuilt engines survived until they were ousted by the diesels, and were withdrawn in 1955–61.

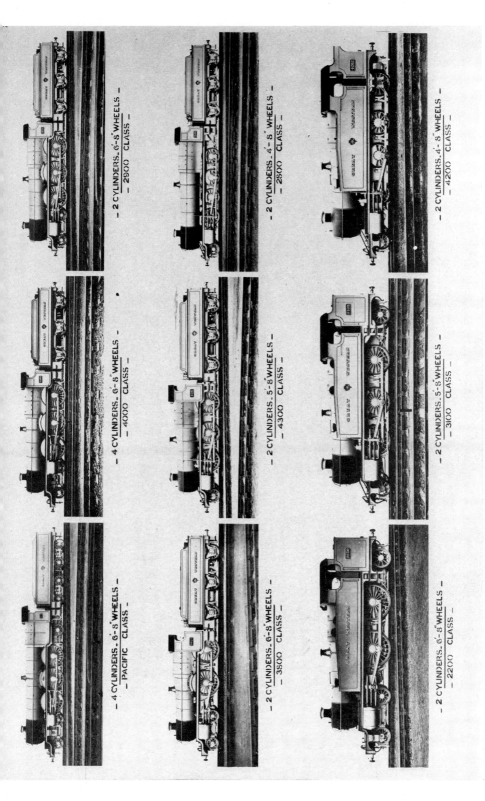

44   Churchward's nine standard locomotive classes. (*British Railways*)

45 *Bird* class 4–4–0
No. 3733 *Chaffinch.*
(*British Railways*)

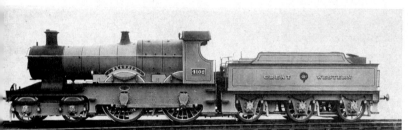

46 *Flower* class 4–4–0
No. 4102 *Begonia.*
(*British Railways*)

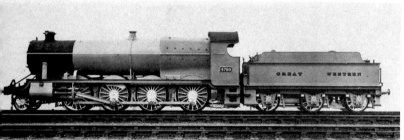

47 Mixed traffic 2–8–0
No. 4700 with large
boiler. (*British
Railways*)

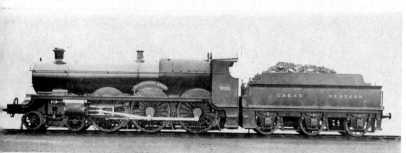

48 The last of the
Churchward line: No.
4061 (*Glastonbury Abbey*
in wartime austerity
livery with cast iron
chimney. (*British
Railways*)

49 12 October 1924.
2–6–2 tank engine
No. 3151 at Rushey
Platt on a Birmingham
local train, composed of
1924 Collett non-
corridor stock. (*British
Railways*)

When Maunsell was appointed CME of the SE&CR the Board decided to divide locomotive responsibilities and to form a separate Locomotive Running Department. To take charge of this they selected A. D. Jones, a former Lancashire & Yorkshire Railway man. He was to be responsible to the CME for the maintenance and running repairs of locomotives, and to the Traffic Manager for providing locomotives suitable for the operation of the various trains.[11]

Maunsell's predecessor had been H. S. Wainwright, who had been appointed Locomotive and Carriage Engineer at Ashford on the formation of the SE&CR in 1899. Under him some very sound classes of engines had been produced to drawings prepared by Robert Surtees, an old London Chatham & Dover Railway man. These were the 'D' and 'E' class 4–4–0s, the 'C' class goods 0–6–0s, the 'H' class 0–4–4 tanks, the small 'P' class 0–6–0 tank engines for rail motor work, and the 'J' class 0–6–4 superheater tanks for heavy suburban working. When Wainwright retired the design for a larger and superheated 4–4–0 (the 'L' class) had been prepared, and the drawings were awaiting dispatch to private locomotive building firms as soon as contracts had been arranged. For some time before his departure Wainwright had been a sick man, with the result that there had been little new construction and the shortage of locomotives had become critical. It was their realisation of this state of affairs that had led the directors to look for a competent engineer with sufficient drive to provide sufficient and adequate locomotives quickly. In his short time at the head of Great Southern & Western locomotive affairs, Maunsell had established a reputation for energy and ability which appealed to the SE&CR Directors, and they accordingly offered him the appointment.

Maunsell came to Ashford in the autumn of 1913. As an outsider, and in view of the terms given to him, he was hardly welcome in the Locomotive Department, and there was no one to assist him in his initial steps.[12]

The shortage of locomotives extended to both passenger and goods traffic. As an interim measure, until new locomotives could be provided, Maunsell borrowed some 2–4–0 engines from the Great Northern Railway, and some 0–6–0s from the Hull & Barnsley Railway. He then sent the drawings of Wainwright's proposed 'L' class to Joynt at the Inchicore drawing office, asking him to have a look at them and suggest any amendments. (At this juncture he preferred to consult his own old drawing office, as he had no knowledge of the competence of the Ashford staff.) Joynt, at that time probably battling against his new chief's preference for long travel and long lap valves, recommended the reduction of the steam lap to $\frac{7}{8}$ inch and a shorter travel. This, and other suggested modifications, were accepted by Maunsell. In adopting this short valve travel Maunsell made a bad mistake. It suited engines having to work the easy schedules of the GS&WR but it was ruinous to fast running. As Holcroft says, 'The "L" class, while being good reliable "old sloggers", would not run at high speed, even downhill. To get 60 m.p.h. or more on down grades necessitated full gear and a "breath of steam" in order to get the exhaust steam away.'[13]

The SE&CR Directors authorised the construction of twenty-two engines of the new 'L' class, with delivery in from six to eight months. British locomotive building firms were particularly busy at this time and only Beyer Peacock could meet the time limit, and that with a maximum of twelve engines. The remaining ten, therefore, were ordered from Borsig of Berlin.

It was now time for Maunsell to consider his own staff. The Chief Locomotive Draughtsman and the Chief Carriage Draughtsman were due to retire shortly. As well as replacements for them, Maunsell wanted a Locomotive Works Manager at Ashford who would also be Assistant CME; and for this last appointment, he wrote to Watson at Inchicore to find out who were available at Swindon. The upshot was that G. J. Churchward persuaded G. H. Pearson, who was then Assistant Carriage Works Manager at Swindon, to accept the post. Pearson was an all-round engineer. After serving his apprenticeship in the Swindon Works, he engaged in a course of study at University College, London. He then entered the Swindon drawing office and took on a variety of work for which the course had qualified him. As one of Swindon's promising young men, he was subsequently for three years an assistant to the Locomotive Works Manager (as Watson was later to become); and in 1905 he was appointed Assistant Carriage Works Manager. By 1913 Pearson had been eight years on the carriage side, and, as no opportunity had arisen or was likely to arise on the Great Western for his further promotion, Churchward evidently thought that he should accept a higher position on another railway.[14]

The other two posts were advertised in *The Engineer* by requesting applications for vacancies as leading draughtsmen. At Swindon Holcroft was also looking for a new job because he had been told that, with the addition of the 43xx class 2-6-0s, no further designs were likely to be undertaken for some years and there was therefore no more development work for him in the locomotive drawing office. After reading the above advertisements, Holcroft promptly applied for the appointment of Leading Locomotive Draughtsman. Shortly afterwards he learned that Pearson had been appointed Assistant CME and Works Manager at Ashford, and so went to tell him of his application. Pearson explained that the post was not quite what it appeared. Robert Surtees, the Chief Locomotive Draughtsman at Ashford, would be retiring in a few months and the advertisement was aimed at somebody to replace him. The SE&CR were thinking of a Midland man from Derby, and in any case he thought that Holcroft was too young to have much of a chance of selection. Nevertheless, in the approaching re-organisation there would be vacancies and he would speak to Maunsell about him.

In the event, Maunsell selected James Clayton from the Midland as Leading Locomotive Draughtsman. Clayton was at that time Assistant Chief Draughtsman at Derby. The carriage post, however, was secured by another Great Western man, Lionel Lynes, who was in charge of the carriage and wagon section of the Swindon drawing office. A little later Holcroft was offered, and he accepted, a job at Ashford, which entailed the execution of plans for the extension and re-organisation of the locomotive, carriage and wagon shops. His farewell to Churchward has already been mentioned,

It was not till the spring of 1914 that matters had settled down sufficiently for the future policy in new locomotive design to be considered. Pearson advocated a mixed traffic 2–6–0 engine on the lines of the Great Western 43XX class. For passenger work he thought that the South Eastern & Chatham, like the London Brighton & South Coast, only needed tank engines, because of the comparatively short distances between London and the coast. If these were of the 2–6–4 type, they could be an elongation of the mixed traffic tender engine, with a bogie to carry the weight of the coal bunker. They would, however, need coupled wheels of a larger diameter.[15]

Maunsell agreed with these proposals, and as soon as Clayton had taken over from Surtees he was told to start on these two types, which were to have many parts in common. The boiler was very much on the lines of the Swindon No. 4, with coned barrel, directly stayed Belpaire firebox, regulator in the smokebox, and an internal steam pipe taking steam from the corners of the firebox. It differed from the Swindon pattern in having a dome, but the purpose of this was to accommodate the top feed, and not to act as a steam collector. The top feed was in the form of a helical shaped chute, instead of the Swindon pattern trays. The superheater header was Maunsell's own design, and the super-heater surface was calculated to produce steam at a temperature of 650°F, which was considerably higher than the moderate superheat favoured by Swindon. Other differences from the 43xx class were the 19 inch by 28 inch cylinders, the 5 foot 6 inch coupled wheels of the 2–6–0, and the outside Walschaerts valve gear. In addition, the framing and cylinder arrangements and the radial truck were entirely different. On the other hand, the Swindon influence was to be seen in the box pistons with flat surfaces front and back, in the solid-bushed big ends of the connecting rods, and in the 10 inch diameter long travel piston valves with internal admission of steam and $1\frac{1}{2}$ inch lap. (How Joynt must have hated to read about this!) The boiler pressure of 200 lb./in.[2] was the same as that of the Great Western engine, whilst the grate area of 25 ft.[2] was much larger. The boiler barrel diameter of 4 feet $7\frac{3}{4}$ inches and 5 feet 3 inches was less than that of the 43xx, but the barrel was 1 foot 6 inches longer. The 2–6–4 tank followed the design of the 2–6–0, except that it had 6 foot coupled wheels and a trailing bogie.[16]

Holcroft considered that the adoption of the same boiler for the tender and tank engines was an error, because its size was dictated by the permitted axle load, and the weight of the full side tanks would not allow of a heavier boiler on the tank engine. As it was, the 2–6–0s, although very good engines, were a little 'shy' for steam, and needed skilful firing to develop their full capacity.

Maunsell's plans for new engines were brought to an abrupt halt by the outbreak of the First World War. The ten German-built 'L' class engines arrived just before it started and the Beyer Peacock batch followed. But the Ashford Works were fully committed to Government war production and could not undertake new construction. In 1917, however, the Railway Executive Committee agreed to the construction of some prototype locomotives, and Maunsell accordingly built the first of the 'N' class 2–6–0s, No. 810, and the 2–6–4 tank engine which, as No. 790, heralded the 'K' class. Both went into service in July 1917.[17] The influence of Derby was apparent in Clayton's design of cab and tender, but the tapered boilers, curved firebox side sheets, top feed, and the run of the footplate clearly showed the Swindon-inspired hand of Pearson. Fifteen more of the 2–6–0 engines were authorised in 1919.

The concessions that the Government had made to the trade unions during the War made it impossible for the smaller railways, such as the SE&CR, to survive independently. The extent to which Maunsell's plans would be realised was therefore in doubt. Nevertheless, many new locomotives would be required by all railways to replace old and run-down stock. In 1917 the Railway Executive Committee requested the Association of Railway Locomotive Engineers to convene a meeting to consider how these needs should be met and to prepare plans. In the opinion of the REC, any locomotives that the ARLE decided on should be built at Woolwich Arsenal in order to give employment during the transition period in which industry would be turning over from war to peace production.

The ARLE appointed a committee under Churchward, consisting of the locomotive engineers of companies represented on the REC. This committee decided on three locomotives types: a 2–6–0 mixed traffic, a 2–8–0 heavy goods, and a 4–4–0 passenger, with priority of construction in that order. The committee appointed a subcommittee under Maunsell to proceed with these proposals. Progress, however, was hampered by the massive amount of paper work that was needed to get agreement. It took so long to circulate minutes and drawings amongst the members of the subcommittee and to obtain approval, that the war was over before any sets of drawings were ready. Nevertheless, it is interesting to compare the principal dimensions of Churchward's 43xx class, the ARLE 2–6–0 design, and Maunsell's 'N' class 2–6–0.

	GWR	ARLE	SECR
Boiler pressure, lb./in.^{2}	200	180	200
Superheater, ft.^{2}	192	254	203
Grate area, ft.^{2}	20·6	25	25
Wheel diameter	5′ 8″	5′ 8″	5′ 6″
Cylinders, inches	$18\frac{1}{2} \times 30$	$20\frac{1}{2} \times 28$	19×28
Piston valve diameter, inches	10	10	10
Valve travel, inches	$6\frac{1}{4}$	$6\frac{3}{4}$	$6\frac{7}{16}$
Valve lap, inches	$1\frac{5}{8}$	$1\frac{1}{4}$	$1\frac{1}{2}$
Weight, tons	62	65	$59\frac{1}{2}$

The similarity between the three designs will be noted, and it is of some interest that at this comparatively early date Churchward's wide piston valves with long travel and lap had won, perhaps grudging, acceptance; though it was not till after the locomotive exchange of 1925 that their importance came to be generally appreciated. The ability of the 'N' class to carry a heavier boiler is shown by a comparison of the weights of the three engines.

The ARLE design never materialised: but to avoid delay in starting work at Woolwich, it was agreed that Maunsell's 'N' class was sufficiently close to the approved design to be acceptable, and it was the most modern of mixed traffic 2–6–0 engines. Orders were accordingly given for 100 sets of parts to be made at Woolwich and for fifty boilers from the North British Locomotive Company. From these, fifty engines were built at Woolwich. However, except for the Southern, none of the new Railway Groups were interested in buying them, preferring to continue, or design, their own mixed traffic locomotives. The Southern bought the whole fifty at a much reduced price and sent them to the West Country to replace the same number of obsolescent London & South Western Railway engines.[18]

There remained the fifty sets of parts without boilers. Of these, the Midland Great Western Railway of Ireland bought twelve in 1924, the Great Southern Railways (formed a short time later by the grouping of the railways wholly within the Irish Free State) bought fifteen, and the Metropolitan Railway bought six which they sent to Armstrong Whitworth for completion as 2–6–4 tank engines. Most of the remaining seventeen sets of parts were bought by the Southern Railway as spares. Boilers for the Irish engines were supplied by Robert Stephenson & Co. to the 'N' class drawings, and these engines were built with longer axles to fit them for the 5 foot 3 inch gauge. The twelve engines completed for the MGWR at their Broadstone Works had 5 foot 6 inch coupled wheels, whilst of the fifteen assembled at Inchicore, the first nine had 5 foot 6 inch wheels and the remaining six had 6 foot wheels. The Broadstone engines were all turned out with a pressure of 200 lb./in.² but the Inchicore engines were only pressed to 180 lb./in.². Bazin told Holcroft that the lower pressure was adopted to save on maintenance, because the 2–6–0s were powerful enough at this pressure for the job they had to do. Later, however, the pressure of the Inchicore engines was also raised to 200 lb./in.².[19]

An interesting aspect of the arrival of the 2–6–0 locomotives in Ireland was that there were now two types of engine running on the Great Southern Railways that had been designed chiefly by Swindon men— Watson's four-cylinder 4–6–0s and Pearson's two-cylinder 2–6–0s. Further, the Churchward influence is also seen in the 4–6–0 mixed traffic locomotives designed by Watson's successor for the Great Southern & Western Railway and built in 1924 (the last engines for that railway before it was absorbed in the Great Southern). Bazin, who was Works Manager at Inchicore from 1919, succeeded Watson in 1921. (Joynt had ceased to be Chief Draughtsman in 1919.) It is conceivable that the disappointing results with the 400 class had been discussed with Swindon. In any case, Bazin's 500 class had 10 inch diameter piston valves with a valve travel of $6\frac{3}{8}$ inches, instead of the $5\frac{1}{4}$ inches of the

400s, and a lap of $1\frac{1}{2}$ inches instead of $1\frac{1}{4}$ inches. Although with their 5 foot 8 inch coupled wheels they were designed primarily for goods work, they were such fast and free running engines that they were used entirely on passenger trains.[20]

This excursion to Ireland has taken us rather ahead of the South Eastern & Chatham scene. At the beginning of 1923, of course, the SE&CR had been absorbed by the Southern Railway, but before that, twenty-two of the 'N' class had been turned out by Ashford, and the appointment of Maunsell as CME of the new railway ensured that Swindon/Ashford practices would predominate in the locomotive department.

A year before the First World War came to an end, the SE&CR decided to make Victoria Station the London terminus for all its boat trains to and from the Channel ports. However, there was a difficulty in that the old London Chatham & Dover line between Victoria and the Chislehurst loops, which connected it to the former South Eastern main Dover line, could not carry locomotives heavier than the Wainwright 'E' class 4–4–0, and the maximum tare weight which this engine could haul on the current schedules was 250 tons. The Traffic Department, apparently asking for the moon, said they wanted an engine which, without weighing more than the 'E' class, could pull 300 tons tare. Maunsell, presumably at Pearson's suggestion, decided to 'Swindonise' the 'E' class. One of them, No. 179, was accordingly taken into Ashford Works for rebuilding. The boiler was given a new Belpaire firebox with sloping back to increase the grate area, and, as in the 'N' class, top feed in the dome with an internal steam pipe and regulator in the smokebox. Long travel 10-inch diameter piston valves, similar to those of the 'N' class were fitted; but the valve heads were fixed $\frac{1}{8}$ inch nearer to one another, producing a steam lap of $1\frac{5}{8}$ inches. At 25 per cent cut-off the openings to steam and exhaust not only exceeded those of the 'N' class, but even those in the Swindon standard layout. These measures led to a very free running and versatile engine; but owing to the heavy blast great care was necessary to prevent the fire from slipping down the sloping grate. The boiler pressure was 180 lb/in^2 and the superheat ranged from 650 to 700°F.[21] Because Clayton was a Midland man, he succeeded in making the rebuilt engine look very much like a Midland class 2 4–4–0, but as compared with this rather sluggish engine, its performance was very different! On test, No. 179 was so outstanding that ten more 'E' class engines were despatched in pairs to Beyer Peacock at Manchester for rebuilding in similar fashion. No. 179

was given pop safety valves, but the others retained their Ramsbottom valves.[22]

Holcroft loved the 'E' class rebuilds and told me they were 'grand engines'. All were in service by 1920, and for some years they handled the Continental traffic with great success, while the Civil Engineer was strengthening the route to carry 4–6–0 engines capable of hauling tare loads of up to 425 tons.[23] The performance of the rebuilt 'Es' (known as the 'E1' class) led to ten of the smaller 'D' class being rebuilt in 1921 in similar fashion and classified 'D1'. This rebuilding was also carried out by Beyer Peacock. The 'D1s' were intended for the Kent Coast trains, and worked these so satisfactorily that another eleven were rebuilt at Ashford in 1922, 1926 and 1927.

The last engine to be built for the SE&CR was designed by Holcroft. In 1908 Holcroft became close friends with R. A. G. Hannington, who was later, as already mentioned, Locomotive Works Manager at Swindon. They formed the idea of using their spare time during the winter evenings to design a locomotive, and decided, after some discussion, on a three-cylinder passenger engine. A problem soon arose over the valve gear for the middle cylinder. They did not like to place it on one side of the centre line, because such a lop-sided arrangement was unacceptable by Swindon standards. They had not spent many evenings over this problem before Hannington was appointed an assistant to the Divisional Locomotive Superintendent and Holcroft was left to carry on by himself. In due course he found a solution by using rocking levers to derive a motion for the inside cylinder from those of the two outside ones. He then built a model which he took to the drawing office and showed to O. E. F. Deverell, the Assistant Chief Draughtsman. The next time that Churchward came into the office he was taken, accompanied by Burrows, to see it. G.J.C. sat down on Holcroft's stool whilst the latter explained his idea and worked the model. Churchward was extremely interested, asked many questions, and finally told Burrows to get the Record Office to apply for a patent. Then he said to Holcroft: 'Now, young man, what you want to do next is to make one valve gear serve for the two valves in a two-cylinder engine, and your fortune's made!'

It was about this time that Holcroft went off on his North American tour. Whilst he was away the Record Office made an extensive search and discovered that a form of conjugated valve gear had been applied to triple expansion marine engines for operating the middle valve. His claim, therefore, could not be stated as original and would have to specify particular ways of operating the middle valve. This would have to be done fairly quickly as time was getting short for the drawing up and lodging of the Complete Specification at the Patent Office. Holcroft was disappointed that his idea was not entirely original, and the consequent loss of enthusiasm together with the need for haste left a loophole in the invention which H. N. Gresley of the Great Northern Railway found a few years later.[24]

During his convalescence from an illness in 1916, Holcroft returned to his invention and built a model which he showed to an interested Maunsell on his return to work. In 1918 Gresley produced a three-cylinder 2-8-0 with a rather elaborate and cumbersome system of operating the inside valve which he described in an article in *The Engineer*. Holcroft wrote a letter to *The Engineer*, showing how a much simpler gear would meet the problem. As a result of this he was invited to apply for membership of the Institution of Locomotive Engineers and to read a paper on three-cylinder locomotives. In November 1918 Holcroft read his paper and was in due course invited by Gresley to visit him. Gresley told Holcroft that he had given him the key to the solution of the problem and that he intended henceforth to build none but three-cylinder engines. This discussion with Holcroft led to the appearance from Doncaster Works in 1920 of Gresley's first three-cylinder 2-6-0, No. 1000 of the 'K3' class. This basic design was used on all future Gresley three-cylinder engines and also in various countries overseas. At first it was referred to as the Gresley-Holcroft arrangement, but in time Holcroft's part in it was forgotten. It is perhaps worth remembering that if it had not been for Holcroft, encouraged by Churchward, Gresley might never have achieved the success which he did. (I once asked Holcroft if he did not think that Gresley had treated him rather unfairly. Harry Holcroft, kindly and generous, as always, replied, 'No; we collaborated.')

Holcroft told Maunsell of his interview with Gresley. Maunsell made no comment at the time, but a week later he said that he had seen Gresley and (apparently in reply to Gresley's wish to have Holcroft at Doncaster) told him that he intended to build three-cylinder engines himself and would need Holcroft's assistance. In due course Maunsell told Holcroft that he wanted him to design a three-cylinder version of the 'N' class, and he instructed Clayton in Holcroft's presence, that he was to be given a completely free hand. And so, in December 1922, three-cylinder 2-6-0 No. 822 was completed, the last SE&CR locomotive before the railway lost its identity on the formation of the

Southern Railway. On test it performed excellently with both a 1000-ton goods train and fast passenger trains. It was a strange, but satisfying, sequel to the Holcroft and Hannington winter-evening sessions at Swindon.

Maunsell's appointment as CME of the Southern Railway led, naturally, to the application of Swindon/Ashford techniques over a far wider field. On the London & South Western Railway Urie had been rebuilding some of Drummond's four-cylinder 4–6–0s as mixed traffic engines. Ten more were awaiting conversion, but the Running Department did not want them for mixed traffic; there was a shortage of express engines, and they asked for them to be rebuilt with larger driving wheels for passenger work. In order to produce them quickly, the 'N15' class of the LSWR was taken as a basis. The new boiler was pressed to 200 lb./in.², and much else was 'Ashfordised' by incorporating such 'N' class features as the smokebox arrangement, superheater header, new $20\frac{1}{2}$ inch by 28 inch cylinders, and long travel valves. These ten were built at Eastleigh and they had the engine bogies and double-bogie tenders from the original Drummond locomotives. The first to appear was No. 453 *King Arthur*, which left Eastleigh Works in February 1925. It was a great and immediate success, but its overall dimensions were too great to fit inside the loading gauge of the old SE&CR.[25]

As there was still an acute shortage of express engines with adequate power, the Board decided to order twenty *King Arthur* type engines from the North British Locomotive Company, but with a modified profile to permit their working over the Eastern Section (that is, the previous South Eastern & Chatham). The corners of the cab were rounded and its roof extended (as in the 'N' class). The Great Western type of vacuum pump was fitted and the tender was the Urie double-bogie type. The order was later increased to thirty engines, and some spare boilers were added. The North British Locomotive Company delivered the first of them in time for the opening of the 1925 summer service, and they took over from the 'E1' class on the route from Victoria to Dover via Tonbridge. The 'E1s' continued to work trains over the alternative routes, which had not yet been strengthened.[26]

When more heavy freight engines were needed, Urie's 'S15' class 4–6–0 express goods engines were taken as the basis, but the engines built were identical with the *King Arthurs*, except for having 5 foot 7 inch coupled wheels, instead of 6 foot 7 inch.

T. S. Finlayson, the Chief Draughtsman at Eastleigh, was akin to Joynt in his dislike of Swindon doctrine. Holcroft says[27] that he clung tenaciously to the Urie practices and would never admit that the *King Arthurs* were any better than the original 'N15' class. Holcroft did not think that Clayton took a sufficiently strong line with him. On several occasions he tried to persuade Clayton to have all the Urie 4–6–0 classes brought into line with the *King Arthurs*, but Finlayson always managed to put him off.

The construction of the four-cylinder *Lord Nelson* class 4–6–0 engines for the Southern marked the end of an era during which two groups of locomotives were designed, following mainly Ashford and Eastleigh practices, respectively. But if the *Lord Nelson* was definitely 'Southern', its construction also diverged somewhat from Churchward practice.[28] Holcroft took part in outlining the design as regards the proportions, but he had no part in the details of construction. If he had had his way the engine would have reflected the detail design of four-cylinder engines as practised at Swindon under Churchward. However, the *Nelsons* were, in his opinion, perhaps the most reliable, trouble-free, and economical of all Southern locomotives, but he thinks they could have been better. The only excuse for mentioning them here is that they were the means whereby certain Swindon characteristics were introduced on the LMS: but this story belongs to the next chapter.

NOTES

1   H. Holcroft, letter to the author.
2   Ibid.
3   Ibid.
4   H. Holcroft, *An Outline of Great Western Locomotive Practice* (London, Locomotive Publishing Co., 1957), p. 138.
5   O. S. Nock, *The G.W.R. Stars, Castles & Kings* (Newton Abbot, David & Charles, 1967), part 1, p. 106.
6   R. N. Clements, 'The GS&WR 400s and 500s', *Journal of the Irish Railway Record Society*, **8** (47), (October 1968).
7   Ibid.
8   Holcroft, *GW Loco. Practice*, p. 138.
9   Clements, op. cit.
10   Ibid.
11   H. Holcroft, letter to the author.
12   Ibid.
13   Ibid.
14   Ibid.
15   Ibid.
16   Ibid.
17   Ibid.
18   Ibid.

19   Ibid.; R.N. Clements, 'The Woolwich Locomotives of the CIE', *Journal of the Irish Railway Record Society*, 5 (23), (Autumn 1958).

20   Clements, *The GS&WR 400s and 500s*; S.J.W., *Locomotives of the Great Southern Railways of Ireland* (London, Arthur H. Stockwell, 1927), pp. 10–11.

21   H. Holcroft, letter to the author.

22   Ibid.

23   Ibid.

24   Ibid.; Holcroft, *Locomotive Adventure* (London, Ian Allan), pp. 65–8.

25   H. Holcroft, letter to the author.

26   Ibid.

27   Holcroft, *Locomotive Adventure*, pp. 138–9.

28   Holcroft, letter to the author.

Chapter 16

From Swindon to Derby and Marylebone

In 1926 it had been sixteen years since *Polar Star* had demonstrated on the West Coast route her tremendous superiority over the express engines of the London & North Western; but the lessons of the 1910 exchange had not really been learned on the 'Premier Line'. C. J. Bowen Cooke had indeed built the four-cylinder 4–6–0s of the *Claughton* class, but they incorporated practically none of the features that had made Churchward's engines so outstanding. There had been no further advance on any of the companies which, in 1923, were amalgamated to form the London Midland & Scottish Railway; and after two hesitant years it was Midland practice, with Sir Henry Fowler as Chief Mechanical Engineer, that dominated the locomotive scene. The Midland Railway had conducted its main line passenger traffic with frequent and light express trains, well within the capacity of its principal express locomotive, the three-cylinder compound 4–4–0. The Midland men believed that that this method of running trains could be extended to all the main line services of the LMS and that the Midland Compound was the engine for the task. It was soon apparent, however, that the North-Western Anglo-Scottish traffic could not be made to fit this pattern, and the express trains leaving Euston for Scotland remained just as heavy as they had been before the Grouping. The LMS, therefore, found itself without a locomotive large enough to meet single handed the needs of the Operating Department. Fowler got busy over the design of a compound Pacific; but the success of the Great Western *Castles* in comparison with the LNER Pacifics, during the exchange running of 1925, had been noted by J. E. Anderson, head of the LMS Motive Power Department. He was opposed to Pacifics, perhaps because of the number of longer turn tables that would be needed, and apparently persuaded his Vice-President chief, J. H. Follows, that a Great Western *Castle* could do the job. As a result, No. 5000 *Launceston Castle* arrived on the LMS in September 1926, and performed with ease the work on

189

which the *Claughtons*, often piloted, lost time. In addition, the coal consumption of the engine, in spite of its low superheat, was better than that of any LMS engine, including the Midland Compound.[1]

In the light of these impressive results, the LMS decided to order fifty similar engines, but Swindon would not supply the drawings. Fowler then turned to Maunsell and asked if he could have drawings of the new *Lord Nelson*. Maunsell agreed and a set was sent from Eastleigh direct to the North British Locomotive Company, who were to develop the design of a new engine in collaboration with Derby.[2]

However, before discussing this new engine it is necessary to relate how the advantages of the Great Western's valve gear design reached the LMS Locomotive Department through quite another channel. In February 1925 two Midland Compounds, each modified experimentally in different ways, were tried against each other on the heavily graded Settle and Carlisle line, hauling the regular Scotch expresses which had been specially increased in weight. One of these engines, No. 1060, had a blast pipe of reduced diameter and a petticoat on the underside of the chimney; whilst the other, No. 1065, had cylinders that had been reduced in diameter to the previous Midland dimensions. Of the two, No. 1065 gave the better performance; but the major interest of the trials lay, not in the results achieved, but in a remarkable paper to which they gave rise.

E. L. Diamond, then a pupil at Derby, conducted an unofficial investigation into the cylinder losses incurred by No. 1065 whilst working on the trials trains. Diamond left the LMS shortly afterwards and joined the staff of the Institution of Mechanical Engineers. There, in 1926, he read a paper before the Graduate Section of the Institution on *An Investigation into the Cylinder Losses in a Compound Locomotive*.[3] It is not proposed to attempt a summary of this brilliant paper, but part of Diamond's conclusions and recommendations are of relevant interest. He pointed out that as great a loss of efficiency occurs in the cylinders as in the boiler, particularly at high speeds; and that cylinder losses increase with the speed, which helps to explain why goods engines run more efficiently than passenger engines. He added that so great is the increase in losses at high speed, due to throttling and back pressure, that he recommended strongly that locomotive tests should not be confined to very heavily graded routes at relatively low speeds, as was so often done, but that they should be made on level or easily graded routes and at high average speeds. Of the facts that he had set forth, he thought that the most important was that in the cylinders of the Midland Compound (known for its high efficiency) the losses due to restricted passages at admission and exhaust increased from 17·6 per cent at 24 m.p.h. to 67·6 per cent at 68 m.p.h., of which probably not more than 15 per cent was necessary for the production of draught. This meant that at 68 m.p.h. an amount of power equal to half the work that was actually exerted on the train was wasted on throttling losses. He thought it was not without significance that one British railway, i.e. the Great Western, which had standardised long lap valves for years past, had a level main line and trains which were scheduled at the highest average speeds. Diamond unhesitatingly recommended, for compound as well as for simple expansion engines, the universal adoption of the long lap valve, by means of which the port opening to steam at admission and exhaust at any given cut-off could be materially increased. He also recommended that in cylinder design the provision of large direct ports and a free exhaust passage should be the first requirement. One wonders whether Joynt and Finlayson were present!

Fowler, who listened to Diamond's paper, was so interested in his conclusions that, when he got back to Derby, he looked at the design for the new LMS 2-6-4 tank engines and told his Chief Draughtsman to design the valve motion afresh to include long travel and long lap valves. When these engines, the 2300 class, appeared in 1927 they soon showed that they were among the fastest and most efficient that had ever run on the lines of the LMSR or its predecessors.[4] But the strangest part of the story is that Fowler, or any other locomotive engineer, should have been surprised at the benefits to be derived from valves with long travel and long lap—benefits which had been demonstrated by Churchward nearly a quarter of a century before! However, it is safe to say that when *Launceston Castle* was borrowed by the LMS part of the reason for Great Western locomotive superiority was known at last.

The new LMS engine, in the design of which the *Lord Nelson* drawings were consulted, was a three-cylinder 4-6-0 with a boiler very similar to that of its Southern cousin,[5] an almost identical firebox, and the same style of cab. The cylinders and valve gear followed Churchward principles but were derived from those of the 2300 class tank engine.[6] The first engine, the *Royal Scot*, gave the type name to the class. In the haulage of the heavy West Coast expresses, the *Royal Scots* were an immediate success, and when the first entered service they were very economical in fuel consumption, showing a saving of 25 per cent per drawbar horsepower per hour as compared with previous locomotives entrusted with this task. In time, however, the wear on the single wide ring of the piston valve head led to leakage and a consequent large increase in coal consumption. The trouble was eventually diagnosed and cured by fitting piston valve heads with six plain narrow rings instead of the single wide ring. The adoption at the start of the Great Western semi-plug piston valves would have saved a lot of trouble and expense. (In connection with these Great Western piston valves, R. F. Hanks says that when R. A. Smeddle went to the Western Region as Mechanical Engineer he 'tried out piston valves with narrow rings on some Western Region engines as he considered the semi-plug valves were unnecessarily elaborate and expensive to produce. He admitted later that they were not so successful and, still puzzled to know why, he quickly reverted to semi-plug valves. I learnt this in conversation with Smeddle.'[7]) Another problem arose through the use of the Midland type axleboxes, because, after some time in service, the engines became very rough riding and there were frequently hot boxes on the coupled axles.[8] But the cure for this had to await the coming of Stanier and the introduction of Great Western axleboxes.

The affair of the *Royal Scots*, involving as it did the rejection of his proposed four-cylinder compound Pacific, did not naturally enhance the prestige of Sir Henry Fowler. In October 1930 he relinquished his position of CME and became Assistant to Sir Harold Hartley, the Vice-President of Engineering and Research, whom Stamp had brought from Oxford to fill the vacancy caused by the death of R. W. Reid. The post of CME was filled temporarily by E. J. H. Lemon, the Carriage & Wagon Superintendent, whilst search was made for a suitable person. Lemon discussed the problem of filling it with a business acquaintance, who made the revolutionary suggestion that the LMS might approach the Great Western and try to secure W. A. Stanier. In due course Stanier was invited to lunch with Sir Harold Hartley and Lemon at the Athenaeum. The eventual result of this lunch was that Stanier took up his position as CME of the LMS on 1 January 1932.[9] The retirement of J. H. Follows left a vacancy for a Vice-President, and into this Lemon was promoted, with responsibility for the Commercial and Operating Departments.

On the Great Western Railway, Stanier had been appointed by Churchward Assistant Locomotive Works Manager at Swindon in 1902, and Works Manager, in succession to Collett, in 1920. In 1922, after Churchward's retirement, he was appointed Works Assistant to the CME, and at the time that he left the Great Western he was Principal

50 The locomotive exchange of 1910. No. 4005 *Polar Star* leaving Euston with the 12.10 Liverpool and Manchester express of the London & North Western Railway. (*British Railways*)

51 An express fish train passing Swindon on 19 October 1921 hauled by mixed traffic 2–6–0 No. 5347. (*British Railways*)

52 Two-cylinder *Saint* class 4–6–0 No. 2973 *Robins Bolitho*, with top feed but still without the Holcroft curves, on a milk train at Addison Road. (*British Railways*)

53 *County* class 4–4–0 No. 3822 *County of Brecon* on an up milk train at Paddington. (*British Railways*)

54 28xx class 2–8–0 on a freight train passing High Wycombe. (*British Railways*)

55 A *Star* class 4–6–0 on an express with a mixture of carriages, including two clerestories and one coach at the end not yet repainted chocolate and cream. (*British Railways*)

56 A *Star* class 4–6–0 on a down express near Twyford in post-Churchward days. (*British Railways*)

57 A 43xx class 2–6–0 with cast iron chimney leaving Old Oak Common for Paddington with coaches for a down express. (*British Railways*)

58 *Star* class 4–6–0 No. 4023 *King George*, one of the *King* series of this class which became the *Monarch* series on the advent of Collett's *King* class in 1927. This engine became *Danish Monarch*. (*British Railways*)

59 The legacy of *The Great Bear* on the LMS. *Princess* class Pacific No. 6203 *Princess Margaret Rose* on the 8.20 a.m. Liverpool to Euston express passing King's Langley on 20 July 1950. (*British Railways*)

Assistant to the CME. Although next in line for the position of CME, he was too close to Collett in age to be able to succeed him.

Churchward was delighted to hear of Stanier's appointment; but Collett seems to have been less enthusiastic. It is alleged that he told Stanier that he would not be able to return to the Great Western if he failed to get on with the LMS authorities because his place would have been filled.

When Stanier entered his office at Euston he was faced with the need for replenishing the LMS stock with a complete range of new locomotives. Midland policy had proved inadequate, and nearly a decade after the formation of the LMS the bulk of its traffic, both passenger and freight, was being worked by either new locomotives which were too small for the hardest jobs, or locomotives inherited from the constituent companies which were rapidly wearing out. These latter comprised a multitude of different types, many of which were of obsolete design.

In 1930 there had been a very successful rebuilding of two London & North Western *Claughtons* with a larger boiler and a three-cylinder chassis similar to that of the *Royal Scot* class. These engines were so good that their performance was very little below *Royal Scot* standard. As an interim measure to meet the pressing requirement for express engines, Stanier, soon after his arrival, had twenty new engines built to the same design in 1932 and thirty more during the next two years. Although nominally *Claughton* rebuilds, these were in fact new engines. The first ten kept the *Claughton* radial bogie, but the remainder incorporated many of Stanier's ideas, including the de Glehn bogie, and Swindon-type axleboxes, wheels and tyres.[10] (The naming of one of these engines, No. 5504 *Royal Signals*, was followed by a regimental guest night in the Officers' Mess of the London Corps Signals, TA, at which Sir William Stanier presented a framed photograph of the engine.)

Stanier then set about planning his new range of locomotives. He was devoted to Churchward and during his early days on the LMS he paid frequent visits to his old chief at 'Newburn' to discuss matters and problems relating to the engines which he proposed to introduce.[11] There is no record unfortunately of the detail of those talks; but when Stanier's locomotives made their appearance it was noted that not only did they incorporate most of Churchward's practices, but they looked like Churchward engines, and the various classes corresponded to those working similar traffic on the Great Western.

The most immediate need was for a really powerful express passenger engine. Trade depression and the competition from road transport were having a severe effect on the Company's revenue, and the LMS had been studying various schemes aimed at both keeping existing traffic and regaining some of that which had been lost to the roads. It had been decided that there should be an increase in the number of express passenger trains and that they should be both faster and more attractive. To compete with the East Coast route, it was thought that the 400 miles between Euston and Glasgow should be covered without a stop, if this was found to be commercially feasible. No existing engine on the LMS, not even a *Royal Scot*, could do this as a regular performance.[12] The provision of such an engine, then, was almost the most pressing task with which Stanier was faced, and it must have been one of the subjects which he discussed on his visits to 'Newburn'.

As we have seen, Churchward had probably envisaged the use of Pacific locomotives to haul the heavy Great Western expresses of the future, and we have noted that the tests of *The Great Bear* were halted by the First World War. Undoubtedly Churchward would have seen a Pacific as the answer to this LMS problem. We can imagine him outlining the lessons which had been learned from *The Great Bear*, and finally perhaps saying: 'Why not take the *King* as a basis and develop it into a Pacific?' Certainly Stanier took a set of drawings of the *King* class with him to Derby. Then, just as Churchward, in his design of *The Great Bear*, took a *Star* as his basis and lengthened the frames to carry a wide firebox and radial truck, so Stanier did the same to derive the *Princess* class Pacific from a *King*. But, profiting by experience with the *Great Bear*, he designed a truck with outside bearings and added a combustion chamber to the boiler.[13] He retained the Swindon low degree of superheat, and there may have been several reasons for this. The LMS 'Pacific' was designed in something of a hurry, so that presumably the less it was necessary to depart from the *King* drawings the better; and in any case the *Kings* had been working well with the Swindon superheater. One departure that Stanier made from Great Western practice was to have four sets of Walschaerts valve gear. It is conceivable that he preferred this arrangement as a result of his experience with the French 'Atlantics' on the GWR; but his selection of it caused some amusement among French engineers. Chapelon wrote: 'It is curious that, after the French compounds had been so criticised for the complications of their four sets of valve gear, which were intended to allow the high pressure and low pressure cut-offs to be adjusted independently, the LMS built twelve Pacific locomotives with four simple expansion cylinders, like those of the Great Western, but having four independent sets of valve gear ... with the object of obtaining greater precision in the regulation of the cutoffs of the four cylinders. It is obvious that in such conditions simple expansion produced no simplification as compared with double expansion and separate high pressure and low pressure cut-offs.'[14] The boiler pressure, cylinder dimensions, and diameter of the coupled wheels of the *Princess* class were the same as those of the *Kings*, and hence the tractive effort was the same.

The external lines of a locomotive are affected to an extraordinary degree by the shape of its chimney. It has, in fact, an influence on the appearance of the whole similar to that of the headdress of a soldier. Stanier presumably did not want a chimney which resembled that of either the London & North Western Railway or the Midland. It has been said that he discussed this with Churchward and that the latter finally said: Why not have one like ours?' Certainly the Stanier chimney had a very Great Western look about it.

Apart from the Pacifics, Stanier had to consider what other standard types were needed. For the heavier express passenger trains there were 122 three-cylinder locomotives of the *Royal Scot* and *Patriot* classes, which were very capable but their mileage between boiler repairs was not very high. (R. C. Bond says that 'when Sir William Stanier rebuilt these locomotives he put a coned barrel on the new boilers, but—what is so much more important—he gave them the shape of the Swindon firebox. The miles between heavy boiler repairs was very nearly doubled.'[15]) Of other useful locomotives, there were 235 mixed traffic 2–6–0s designed and built at Horwich, seventy-five of Fowler's new 2–6–4 tank engines, the ex-LNWR G2 class 0–8–0s for heavy goods, and the Midland type class 4 0–6–0 engines for light goods.

Stanier decided on six new types of locomotive (in addition to the Pacifics), all of which should have Swindon-type taper boilers and fireboxes, in order to reduce the costs of maintenance and increase the mileage between repairs. All of these six new classes had their equivalent in Great Western types in current use. One was a 4–6–0 express engine, which might be compared with a *Star* or *Castle*. It had, however, three cylinders, perhaps because of their use in the very successful *Patriots* from which this design was developed. Engines of this class, later styled *Jubilee*, were initially designated at Crewe as *Claughton* replacements. There was another 4–6–0 with two cylinders and coupled wheels 6 feet in diameter which was equivalent to a Great Western *Hall*, and was called by Crewe a *Prince* replacement. In reference to their power class and colour, they were later nicknamed the *Black Fives* (to distinguish them from the *Jubilees*, which were painted maroon). For heavy goods there was a 2–8–0 to replace the LNWR G2s, which was inspired by Churchward's 28xx class 2–8–0, and the demand for more of the excellent Horwich 2–6–0s was met by a Swindonised version, equivalent to the Churchward 43xx class. Finally the 2–6–4 and 2–6–2 tank engines were continued by taper boilered types with a marked affinity to the Great Western larger 2–6–2 tanks. The range of boilers for these new engines was probably Stanier's greatest success. The detail design was done by J. L. Francis, draughtsman at Crewe, who had started his apprenticeship in the same month and year as R. A. Riddles, and to whom Stanier himself gave full credit.[16]

Stanier's engines came out rapidly. The first Pacific appeared in August 1933. This was a few months before Churchward's death, and it seems likely that at Stanier's invitation he would have travelled to Euston to see it. The second Pacific was ready soon after the first; but the 2–6–0s were actually the first of Stanier's classes to arrive in traffic, fifteen being ready in 1933 and the remaining twenty-five in 1934. The biggest delivery in 1934 consisted of eighty-four *Jubilees* and in the same year there were the first twenty of the *Black Fives*, as well as thirty-seven three-cylinder 2–6–4 tanks, designed for quick acceleration on the London Tilbury & Southend line. Eleven more Pacifics came out in 1935, of which one was turbine driven. Also in 1935 there were turned out no less than 205 *Black Fives* and the first twenty-two of the 2–8–0 heavy goods locomotives. Other 1935 additions were eight 2–6–4 tank engines, but this time with two cylinders, and seventy-four of the smaller 2–6–2 variety. The monumental 1935 construction was completed by forty-eight more *Jubilees*; the final sixty of this class being turned out the following year. This tremendous programme was virtually finished in 1936 with 100 *Black Fives*, forty-two 2–8–0s, 116 two-cylinder 2–6–4 tank engines, and seventy-four 2–6–2 tanks.[17]

One Swindon practice which did not last long was a low degree of superheat. For its success it depended on perfect steaming and full pressure in the boiler, together with the excellent Welsh coal and first class firing. If any of these conditions were not met, there was no reserve, and steam was down to saturation point before expansion had been completed. The Pacifics did not steam as freely as had been hoped and expected, and early in 1935 *The Princess Royal* was fitted with a new boiler having double the superheater surfaces of the previous one. The result was excellent, and all Stanier's engines were eventually given high superheat. With the lubricating oils that were now available, there was none of the trouble from carbonisation that had been experienced on the London & North Western *Georges*, *Princes* and *Claughtons*.

That Stanier regarded his engines as developments of those designed by Churchward is shown by the following incident related to me by R. F. Hanks. He wrote to congratulate Sir William Stanier on the splendid performance of one of his 2–8–0 locomotives on the London Midland Region of British Railways when it was put on an express train to replace a diesel that had failed. With typical modesty, says Hanks, Stanier replied, 'Give the credit to G. J. Churchward and the Great Western.'[18]

Subsequent design on the LMS produced engines that continued the logical development of Churchward's ideas, and when the railways were nationalised in 1948 the locomotive stock of that company was, on the whole, the soundest and most modern in the country. Nevertheless, the war years had taken their toll, and when R. A. Riddles was appointed Member for Mechanical & Electrical Engineering on the Railway Executive he was faced with the task of providing engines which, though incorporating all that was best in modern practice, should be simple to drive, easy to maintain, and able to run with indifferent fuel. How he set about the job has been told elsewhere[19] and it is not really part of the Churchward story. But the ancestry of his engines was plain to see. In the discussions that followed Sir William Stanier's reading of his paper on G. J. Churchward to the Newcomen Society, R. C. Bond said that: 'there was no other engineer whose work could still be seen so plainly running about the country as Mr Churchward's. There were not only the Great Western locomotives—there were Sir William's own London Midland & Scottish locomotives and, later still, the British Railways standard series.'[20]

NOTES

1   E. S. Cox, *Locomotive Panorama*, vol. I (London, Ian Allan, 1965), pp. 55–6; Colonel H. C. B. Rogers, *The Last Steam Locomotive Engineer; R. A. Riddles, C.B.E.* (London, George Allen & Unwin, 1970), p. 52.
2   H. Holcroft, *Locomotive Adventure* (London, Ian Allan), p. 141.
3   *Proceedings of the Institution of Mechanical Engineers* (1927).
4   Cox, op. cit., p. 58; O. S. Nock, *The Midland Compounds* (Newton Abbot, David & Charles, 1964), pp. 82–87.
5   Holcroft, op. cit., p. 141.
6   Cox, op. cit., p. 59.
7   R. F. Hanks, letter to the author.
8   Cox, op. cit., p. 87.

9 Rogers, op. cit., pp. 60, 61; R. C. Bond, information to the author.

10 Cox, op. cit., pp. 68, 105; R. C. Bond, information to the author.

11 O. S. Nock, *Sir William Stanier* (London, Ian Allan, 1964), p. 62.

12 Rogers, op. cit., p. 62.

13 H. Holcroft, letter to the author.

14 A. Chapelon, *La Locomotive à Vapeur* (Paris, J. B. Baillière et Fils, 2nd edn, 1952), pp. 50, 51.

15 Sir William Stanier, 'George Jackson Churchward, Chief Mechanical Engineer, Great Western Railway', *Transactions of the Newcomen Society* (1955)—discussions on the paper.

16 Rogers, op. cit., p. 65.

17 Rogers, op. cit., pp. 76, 77.

18 R. F. Hanks, letter to the author.

19 Rogers, op. cit., pp. 169f

20 Stanier, op. cit.

Chapter 17

Churchward's Achievement

In order to assess Churchward's achievement and his status as a loco-motive engineer, one should perhaps describe his work against the background of contemporary locomotive practice, from the time that he first contributed to locomotive design, and show how his methods and ideas influenced engineers of other railways, both during his time on the Great Western and after his departure.

When Churchward entered the Locomotive Works at Swindon in December 1895 as Assistant Works Manager, most railways were using, or were about to use, 4–4–0 inside cylinder simple expansion engines for the haulage of their express passenger trains. The majority of goods trains were worked by 0–6–0 engines, also with inside cylinders, and there was a variety of mainly inside cylinder tank engines for local passenger and freight trains. This generalisation, however, did not apply to all railways and still less to all trains. The single driver with leading bogie or radial axle was still common, particularly on the Great Northern, the Midland, the North Eastern, and the Great Western itself; on the London & South Western and the Highland many of the 4–4–0s had outside cylinders; and compounds of various types were in use for all types of traffic on the London & North Western and the North Eastern. On the whole most engines did, with reasonable competence, the job for which they were designed, if without any particular brilliance or efficiency. A study of their dimensions shows that there was little basic difference between most of them, and they conformed generally to similar patterns of construction. Whilst many locomotive engineers tried to restrict the number of different types of locomotives on their railways, there was, with one exception, little attempt at standardisation of parts between locomotive types. Towards the end of the century there was a marked move by some railway companies towards the con-struction of much bigger engines to meet the demands of traffic depart-ments for more power to work the heavier trains that they wished to run.

199

In August 1895 there had taken place the great railway race between the East and West Coast routes from London to Aberdeen. Churchward no doubt followed this with great interest and derived his own lessons from it. On the Great Northern section of the East Coast route, Patrick Stirling's famous 'eight-foot singles' with outside cylinders hauled the trains from King's Cross to York. These 4–2–2s were first built in 1870, and Stirling continued their production, with various modifications, until his death in 1895. They were fast and free-steaming engines, but their boilers were too small for the needs of the time and their performances on the racing trains were not outstanding. On the rival route, south of Crewe, the trains were worked by the best of F. W. Webb's three-cylinder compounds with four uncoupled driving wheels, the 2–2–2–0 *Teutonics*. They too performed adequately on the light racing trains, but without particular brilliance. North of York and Crewe it was a very different story. Wilson Worsdell's new 'M' class simple expansion 4–4–0s ran brilliantly between York and Edinburgh. With a train weighing 105 tons, No. 1620 covered the distance of 124·5 miles from Newcastle to Edinburgh in 113 minutes start to stop, at an average speed of 66·1 m.p.h., including something over 90 m.p.h. down Cockburnspath bank. The highlight of West Coast running was the work of Webb's *Precedent* class simple expansion 2–4–0 engines between Crewe and Carlisle. With a very light train of 70·5 tons tare, No. 790 *Hardwicke* covered this difficult route, including the climb over Shap, in 126 minutes for the 141 miles, an average speed of 67·2 m.p.h. These little *Precedents*, indeed, started a tradition, which lasted till the end of the London & North Western's separate existence, of small engines that could be flogged along at high speeds, though at some considerable expense in maintenance and fuel. North of the Border the trains were worked successfully by inside cylinder 4–4–0s of basically Dugald Drummond design. On the North British they had been built by Holmes and on the Caledonian by Drummond himself and by his successor Lambie. (Dugald Drummond at this time had just succeeded Adams as Mechanical Engineer of the London & South Western Railway.)

Many North Eastern passenger trains were still hauled by the two-cylinder compound locomotives, both 4–4–0 and 4–2–2, designed by Wilson Worsdell's elder brother and predecessor, T. W. Worsdell. One of the latter's big 'J' class singles, built between 1888 and 1890, had run at a speed of 86 m.p.h. on level track with a train of eighteen of the light carriages of the period. This was the first instance of so high a speed in Great Britain. Wilson Worsdell, in 1899, produced his very successful

'R' class 4-4-0s with piston valves $8\frac{3}{4}$ inches in diameter and boilers with a diameter of 4 feet 9 inches. In the same year he built his 'S' class, the first passenger 4-6-0 locomotives in the country. They had coupled wheels of the comparatively small diameter of 6 foot, boilers with a diameter of 4 feet 9 inches, and shallow fireboxes. They were not very successful and were soon relegated to express goods work. The following year Worsdell turned out his 'S1' class 4-6-0s, which were very similar to the 'S' class but which had piston valves and larger coupled wheels of 6 foot $8\frac{1}{4}$ inch diameter. They were better than their predecessors, but did not last long on the best trains.

On the North Eastern's southern partner, the Great Northern, H. A. Ivatt succeeded Patrick Stirling and was soon building bigger engines. In 1898 came the first British Atlantic, No. 990 which, with its coupled wheels placed very close together, was almost a coupled version of Patrick Stirling's 'singles'. No. 251, the first of Ivatt's large boiler Atlantics, with the wide firebox which excited Churchward's interest, appeared in 1902.

In 1899 Sir John Aspinall of the Lancashire & Yorkshire Railway brought out a big Atlantic which had the peculiarity, for that type, of inside cylinders. It had coupled wheels with the large diameter of 7 feet 3 inches, semi-balanced slide valves, a larger port area than usual, and a free passage for the exhaust. The result was a fast and very capable engine. Ten years earlier the first of Aspinall's famous 2-4-2 tank engines, which were used on short distance express services for so many years, steamed away from Horwich—the first engine, indeed, to be built at Horwich.

The cult of the large boiler had really been initiated on the Caledonian, when in 1896 J. F. McIntosh completed his 4-4-0 No. 721 *Dunalastair*, with a boiler of 4 feet $9\frac{1}{4}$ inches in diameter, instead of the normal 4 feet 4 inches or 4 feet 2 inches. It was basically a Drummond engine with a bigger boiler. Engines of this class were followed by two similar, but progressively larger, types of 1897 and 1899 of which the latter had a boiler pressure of 200 lb./in^2.

David Jones was one of the great individualist locomotive engineers of his time, and his engines, with their outside cylinders and stovepipe chimneys with horizontal louvres in their outer casing, could not be mistaken for those of anybody else. His *Loch* class 4-4-0s of 1896 were the first Highland Railway engines to have piston valves; but he is best known for his 4-6-0 'Goods' engines of 1894, the first of that wheel arrangement in Great Britain. Though, with their 5 feet 3 inch coupled wheels, they were classified 'goods', they regularly handled the heaviest passenger trains between Perth and Inverness. Peter Drummond, who succeeded Jones, returned to his brother's more conventional outline with his *Ben* class inside cylinder 4–4–0s of 1898. However, his *Castle* class 4–6–0s of 1900, with outside cylinders and 5 feet 9 inch coupled wheels were, except for the Drummond chimney, remarkably similar to the Jones 'Goods', and indeed were said to have been designed by him before the accident which led to his resignation.

William Adams, on the London & South Western Railway, also favoured outside cylinders, and the trial runs of his excellent 4–4–0s are discussed later. Dugald Drummond, who succeeded him, reverted to inside cylinders for his two-cylinder engines.

On the important Midland Railway, S. W. Johnson was building inside cylinder 4–4–0 and 4–2–2 passenger engines up to 1900. Some of the former, built in that year, had Belpaire fireboxes, the first Midland locomotives to be so equipped; but the chief event of this period was the appearance in 1901 of the first of his five three-cylinder compound 4–4–0s.

Most good trains, as has been said, were worked by 0–6–0 engines, but 0–8–0s were appearing on some railways. For the North Eastern Wilson Worsdell had built his famous 'T' class with outside cylinders and piston valves. Webb had both three-cylinder and four-cylinder compound coal 0–8–0s on the London & North Western in large numbers. Ivatt was building his 401 class for the Great Northern and Aspinall his 500 class for the Lancashire & Yorkshire.

It will suffice to close this short survey of locomotive practice at the end of the nineteenth century with a mention of J. Holden's work on the Great Eastern Railway. It will be remembered that from 1882 to 1885 Churchward was Assistant Carriage Works Manager with Holden as his chief. Holden in 1885 left the Great Western to become Locomotive Superintendent of the Great Eastern Railway. There he built engines with steam pipes and regulators that were exceptionally large in relation to the cylinders in order to get a good steam circuit. But in addition to this excellent design feature, he introduced a considerable degree of standardisation, after making a careful study of the interchangeability of parts. It is true that Aspinall was doing much the same sort of thing at Horwich for the Lancashire & Yorkshire, but Holden went much further. Boilers, cylinders, axles, axleboxes, motion, and other components were the same for his 2–2–2 and 2–4–0 express engines (these two classes being identical except for the wheel arrangement), his 2–4–0 mixed traffic engines, his goods 0–6–0s, and 2–4–2 tanks.[1] These were built from 1886 onwards, and it is conceivable that both standardisation and steam circuits were discussed between Churchward and Holden when they were together in the Carriage Works. Holden's masterpiece was probably the 1900, or *Claud Hamilton* class 4–4–0s with inside cylinders, of which the first was turned out in 1900. Apart from its efficiency, it had a remarkable beauty of line, which was well set off by the Great Eastern dark blue livery and the brass cap to the chimney which Holden, probably inspired by the Great Western copper cap, had now adopted. Mention must be made, too, of his ingenious and successful attempt to prove that steam traction could equal electric in acceleration, by the building in 1903 of his big 0–10–0 *Decapod* tank engine.

In the light of contemporary practice, Churchward's plan of 1901 for six standard locomotives, with many common components, seems all the more remarkable. At a time when 4–6–0 locomotives were making only a tentative appearance on British railways, he selected them as his standard express type; and when other engineers were building the 0–6–0 type for freight traffic, and were moving towards the 0–8–0 for the heavier trains, Churchward rejected both and chose the 2–8–0 as the standard for goods and mineral traffic. It is significant that Churchward never designed an engine without either a leading bogie or pony truck; for he was entirely opposed to an engine having unguided coupled wheels. It was many years before other locomotive engineers followed him in this respect, but Stanier did so on the LMS and Riddles continued the same practice for British Railways. Furthermore, Churchward's standard types of 1901 were the basis, not only of those locomotive classes built to work Great Western traffic for the remainder of that railway's existence, but also of those ultimately developed for the London Midland & Scottish and for British Railways. Apart from Holden, no other locomotive engineer achieved a similar degree of standardisation of locomotive types. The boldness of Churchward's selection of standard locomotives is emphasised by the failure of such eminent locomotive engineers as Wilson Worsdell on the North Eastern, Dugald Drummond on the London & South Western, and J. G. Robinson on the Great Central, to build good 4–6–0 engines.

In assessing the reason for the excellence of Churchward's locomotives one might well start with the great care that was taken in the smallest aspect of design and manufacture, and the very high standard of workmanship on which he insisted. The very appearance of his engines aroused the admiration of an engineer. R. A. Riddles remembers the *Polar Star* arriving at Crewe in 1910. He says, 'I saw this beautiful engine come into the station—the paint immaculate, the motion beautifully machined, and the footplate fittings polished. The engine not only *was* good, it *looked* good.'[2]

It was the boiler of a Churchward locomotive which probably had the greatest impact on the casual observer; and indeed the boiler and firebox which he designed were by far the most efficient and trouble-free in the country. At the end of the nineteenth century the typical British locomotive boiler was from 4 feet 2 inches to 4 feet 4 inches in diameter with a round flush-topped firebox, a dome and a parallel barrel. Some engines had a raised firebox to obtain extra steam space, and on the Great Northern and South Eastern, for instance, the boilers were domeless. Boiler pressures were generally about 150 lb./in.[2]; sometimes as low as 140 lb./in.[2], and occasionally as high as 175 lb./in.[2]. These conventional and 'conservative' boilers were frequently good steam raisers, but the cost of their maintenance was generally high and was only kept within bounds by the low steam pressures. The expense of their upkeep mounted with increased boiler pressures and, as already stated, this was demonstrated in the difference in maintenance costs between the original *Royal Scots* and the rebuilt engines with a Churchward type boiler. And on the Great Northern Railway (Ireland) the three-cylinder compounds of 1932 lost much of their brilliance when the high cost of maintaining their boilers led to a reduction in the pressure.

The steps in the development of the Churchward boiler and the thorough investigations that accompanied them have already been described. Churchward founded his design on American practice. In the 1890s the so-called 'wagon top' boiler was very much favoured on the other side of the Atlantic. In this type the wrapper plate of the outside firebox was united to the barrel of the boiler by a conically flanged saddle plate. This allowed the crown of the outside firebox to be raised and so increase the steam space above the inner firebox. Many engines with this type of boiler had, too, a Belpaire firebox.[3]

In his paper on *Large Locomotive Boilers* of 1906, Churchward explained the reasons behind the design of his boilers as boilers as follows:

'On the Great Western Railway less trouble has been experienced with the flat-top firebox than with the round top. ... The flat top has the important advantage of increasing the area of the water-line at the hottest part of the boiler, and so materially contributes to the reduction of foaming. This, combined with the coned connection to the barrel, has enabled the dome, always a source of weakness, to be entirely dispensed with and drier steam obtained. . . . The liberal dimension of 2 feet between the top of the firebox and the inside of the casing no doubt contributed to this satisfactory result. The coned barrel connection, in addition to providing a greater area of water line, also gives a larger steam capacity, and, by the larger diameter being arranged to coincide with the line of the firebox tube plate, much more water space at the sides of the tubes is possible. On consideration of the great intensity of temperature at the firebox tube plate, as compared with that at the smokebox plate, the advantage of the arrangement is obvious.'

The boilers designed by Stanier for the LMS and by Riddles for BR were basically the same as those so simply described by Churchward in 1906. After 1906 there were, of course, Churchward's later improvements of top feed, superheat, and the tapering of the barrel from the throat plate to the front end. Whether, if the 1914 War had not interfered with development, Churchward would have profited by the better oils available, to install greater superheat, we do not know. Whilst his engines could work the existing traffic to the speeds required, there was probably little advantage to be gained by increasing superheat with a consequent increase in maintenance costs. On the other hand, if the last batch of *Stars*, the *Abbeys*, had been given a greater degree of superheat it might not have been necessary to build the *Castles*, which were admittedly a compromise. However, the *Abbeys* appeared after Churchward had retired.

Of the firebox, Stanier said: 'The squareness of the firebox gave way to curved side plates and crown, and Churchward spent a great deal of time in developing the curvature of the side plates in order to obtain free circulation and to permit expansion of the firebox and casing with minimum stay stress.'[4] This one sentence is sufficient answer to those critics who claim that Churchward copied the work of other engineers, rather than produce original work of his own. What he did in fact do was to take sound ideas or equipments from anywhere or anyone and employ them to serve his own genius in design.

Churchward has been criticised, too, for the very long tubes which he put into the boiler of *The Great Bear*; but this criticism is anticipated by the following statement in his paper on *Large Locomotive Boilers*:

'The extended length of tubes seen in some designs of wide firebox boilers is due to the use of six-coupled wheels in front of the firebox.

Experience of long tubes appears to be quite satisfactory, and they certainly keep up the economical efficiency of the boiler when it is being forced to the limit of its capacity. In this respect the long tube fulfils the same function as the Serve tube (which is favoured so much on the Continent) performs in boilers with shorter barrels. The ratio of diameter to length of the tube undoubtedly has a most important bearing upon the steaming qualities of the boiler, and upon the efficiency of the heat absorption. This is more particularly noticeable when the boilers are being worked to the limit of their capacity.'

But if the boiler was the most distinctive feature of Churchward's locomotives, it is at least arguable that in the design of his valve gear, and, indeed, the whole of his steam circuit, he made an even more notable contribution to locomotive design. At the time when Churchward became Assistant Locomotive Works Manager, all too little attention had been paid to these matters. Most engines had slide valves with a travel of less than four inches and a lap of about 1 inch. As a result if they were run in the theoretically most economical way, with a short cut-off and fully opened regulator, the admission and exhaust of the cylinder steam was throttled and there was considerable back pressure in the cylinders. Consequently the normal method of working was with a longer cut-off and a partially opened regulator, through which throttling losses also occurred. Fuel consumption in either case was higher than it would have been with well designed long travel valve gear.

However, the locomotives of one engineer were to some extent an exception. William Adams of the London & South Western Railway was probably the most able of British locomotive engineers in the pre-Churchward era. He was Mechanical Engineer of the LSWR from 17 January 1878 till 1 July 1895; thus vacating his appointment before Churchward became Locomotive Works Manager. Adams's finest engines were the sixty 4–4–0 express locomotives which were turned out from the Nine Elms Locomotive Works between 1890 and 1895. They were in four classes: 'X2' of twenty engines with 7 feet 1 inch coupled wheels, built 1892–93; 'T3' of twenty engines with 6 feet 7 inch wheels, built 1892–93; 'T6' of ten engines with 7 feet 1 inch wheels, built 1895–96; and 'X6' of ten engines with 6 feet 7 inch wheels, built 1895–96. The engines with the smaller coupled wheels were intended, as was the normal practice on the London & South Western, for working over the heavy gradients between Salisbury and Exeter. In July 1891 a series of trials were carried out with 'X2' class 4–4–0 No. 582.

Although, within the standards of the times, these Adams 4–4–0s were exceptionally well built, they were, except for their outside cylinders, generally typical of contemporary practice. In the very comprehensive list of dimensions of these and many other locomotives running in Great Britain in 1895, provided by W. F. Pettigrew,[5] there is none peculiar to Adams's engines. They had, however, two unusual features; one was the excellent bogie designed by Adams and the other was his 'Vortex' blast pipe. This ingenious device had an outer annular orifice for steam and an internal circular funnel for the gases; the latter forming the upper portion of a bell-mouthed scoop which was open to and faced the bottom rows of boiler tubes. This arrangement allowed the exhaust steam to be emitted at a lower velocity than with the ordinary blast pipe, and the area of its escape was so proportioned as to reduce the back pressure on the piston to a minimum. The reduction of the velocity resulted in a more uniform flow of air through the fire, so that no holes were formed in it, even if it was thin, and no large cinders were expelled from the chimney. The eminent French engineer, André Chapelon, has a very high opinion of this Vortex blast pipe. Of it he writes:[6] 'A very remarkable exhaust, which perhaps attracted insufficient attention at the time, is the Vortex blast pipe, or the Adams system of annular exhaust, the fitting of which to London & South Western locomotives started in 1885, and with which more than 500 locomotives of this railway and many French locomotives of the Nord and Ouest Companies were eventually equipped.' Chapelon continues that it answered the four main requirements of an exhaust: a low back pressure on the piston; a draught which was at such a level as to allow the pressure and water level to remain constant in the boiler; an automatic adjustment so that it was effective at all power outputs; and an action which allowed the fire to burn equally over the whole surface of the grate, resulting in the highest combustion efficiency. He concludes: 'The fouling of the annular blast pipe seems to have been the sole reason that this excellent arrangement was, rather prematurely moreover, abandoned.'

The trials with No. 582 consisted of five runs with trains of different weights from, respectively, London to Bournemouth, Bournemouth to London, London to Exeter, Exeter to Woking, and London to Salisbury. A striking feature for the time was that the engine was driven with regulator fully open at speed and with a short cut-off. For instance, a cut-off of 17 per cent was recorded at 68 m.p.h. down a gradient of 1 in 251, at 66 m.p.h. down 1 in 386, and at 78 m.p.h. down 1 in 100. But even more striking was the low coal consumption. On the first run the coal used per indicated horsepower hour was 1·98 pounds. The maximum recorded was 2·39 pounds on the second run; the others being between these two figures. No. 582 was burning Welsh coal similar to that used on the Great Western Railway.[7]

Although the trials were held in 1891, it was some years before the results were reported to the outside world. An account was eventually given in a paper presented to the Institution of Civil Engineers by W. Adams, in collaboration with his Locomotive Works Manager at Nine Elms, W. F. Pettigrew, and recorded in their Proceedings of 1895–96. This paper was read shortly before Churchward became Works Manager at Swindon and it is quite likely that he was amongst those listening to it; but if not, he would undoubtedly have read it himself later. He knew, therefore, that it was possible, even with existing valve settings, to work with full regulator and short cut-off, with consequent low coal consumption. It would have been apparent to him that, as No. 582 incorporated no other abnormal features in its design, the result must have been due entirely to the Vortex blast pipe. At the same time, the published indicator diagrams showed the throttling that one would expect from the small port openings obtained by short travel valves at such a reduced cut-off.

We may suggest, therefore, that Churchward believed he could get results similar to those of Adams, but with much less loss of power, by designing a valve arrangement to give wide port openings and by using, like Holden (with whom he may well have discussed it), steam pipes of large diameter to provide a good steam circuit from regulator to exhaust. He may have thought of adopting the Vortex blast pipe, but have rejected it because of the fouling which Chapelon mentions.

Churchward, then, with the information which we have shown was at his disposal, decided to get his large port openings at short cut-off by using long travel valves with long laps. But of course it is one thing to decide on a system in theory and quite another to put it into successful practice; and it was the brilliant design of Churchward's valve arrangements that produced such astounding results. His engines were just as economical as those of Adams in coal consumption and their loss of power from throttling was far smaller. (In view of the paper by Adams and Pettigrew, it is strange that the LMS found it so difficult to believe the figure of 2·1 pounds of coal per indicated horsepower hour which, as the Great Western announced in 1925, had been achieved by No. 4074 *Caldicot Castle*.[8]) All locomotive engineers in Great Britain eventually followed Churchward in the use of long travel and long lap valves; though, as we have seen, it was a quarter of a century before the practice became universal. In the end it became such a commonplace of design that a younger generation of locomotive engineers would never have contemplated using a valve with a short travel.

The final major item that contributed to the success of Churchward's engines was stated as follows by Stanier:[9] 'Churchward was a great believer in large bearing surfaces, and right from the beginning his standard engines had large journals and the bearings were so designed that they had a running clearance on each side to build up the oil film with a proper wool and horsehair pad to keep the journal flooded with oil, so that his engines were remarkably free from trouble with hot boxes.' When Sir William himself took these same practices to the London Midland & Scottish the incidence of hot boxes on that railway was much reduced.

Churchward astonishes one both in the wide range of his genius and in the meticulous research and design which, together with his insistence on high standards of construction, ensured the pre-eminence of his locomotives. In boilers, fireboxes, valve gear, steam circuit, top feed, bearing surfaces, and in standardisation of locomotives and their components, he influenced decisively all modern British locomotive design. In the long line of British locomotive engineers, George Stephenson alone exercised a comparable influence. Overseas one can think of no one who excelled him except André Chapelon, and this very great man, writing to me on various aspects of Churchward's work, concludes: 'The *Star* was succeeded in 1923 by the *Castle*, an engine of high reputation; then in 1927 came the still more powerful *King*, from which Stanier's Pacifics inherited the same arrangement of the engine. Such a succession of locomotives on the same system demonstrates the excellence of the productions of the great engineer that Churchward was. This information probably duplicates some of that you already have; *mais* (I think it appropriate to finish in the original French) *j'ai pensé exprimer ainsi mon admiration pour ce grand ingénieur de locomotives.*'[10] Churchward would I think have appreciated that.

NOTES

1 W. F. Pettigrew, *A Manual of Locomotive Engineering* (London, Charles Griffin & Co., 2nd edn revised, 1901), pp. 36–39.
2 Colonel H. C. B. Rogers, *The Last Steam Locomotive Engineer: R. A. Riddles, C.B.E.* (London, George Allen & Unwin, 1970), p. 30.
3 Pettigrew, op. cit., pp. 318, 340.

4   Sir William Stanier, 'George Jackson Churchward, Chief Mechanical Engineer, Great Western Railway, *Transactions of the Newcomen Society* (1955).

5   Pettigrew, op. cit., Appendix B.

6   A. Chapelon, *La Locomotive à Vapeur* (Paris, J. B. Baillière et Fils, 2nd edn, 1952), pp. 132, 133.

7   Pettigrew, op. cit., pp. 288–313.

8   E. S. Cox, *Locomotive Panorama*, vol. I (London, Ian Allan, 1965), p. 44; O. S. Nock, *The London & South Western Railway* (London, Ian Allan, 1956), p. 67.

9   Stanier, op. cit.

10   A. Chapelon, letter to the author.